TRACKS IN THE SNOW

1. HENRY FUSELI. Painting

RUTHVEN TODD

TRACKS IN THE SNOW

STUDIES IN
ENGLISH SCIENCE AND ART

For being too hasty in huddling up and
tumbling out Books. Herein I confess I
cannot acquit my self wholly from blame.
I know well, that the longer a Book lies by
me, the perfecter it becomes. Something
occurs every day in reading or thinking,
either to add, or to correct and alter for
the better; but should I defer the Edition
till the Work were absolutely perfect, I
might wait all my life-time, and
leave it to be published by
my Executors.

JOHN RAY
Miscellaneous Discourses
1692

LONDON
THE GREY WALLS PRESS

FOR
John Piper
AND
Geoffrey Grigson
WITH LOVE
AND
GRATITUDE

First published in 1946
by The Grey Walls Press Limited
7 *Crown Passage, Pall Mall, London, S.W.*1
Printed in Great Britain
at The Curwen Press Limited
Plaistow, London

CONTENTS

LIST OF ILLUSTRATIONS

The photographs for plates 2, 4, 5, 7, 8, 9, 12, 13, 14, 16, 21, 23, 24, 35, 37, 41, and for the text figures, were taken by Alfred Carlebach, F.R.P.S.

ILLUSTRATIONS IN THE TEXT

NOTE

I am painfully aware that this book displays an ignorance that is both crass and astonishing. There are so many things which I should have known; I can plead nothing in extenuation beyond the fact that I have done my best to explore some roads left unregarded by most other people. These roads seemed to me to be worth following.

During the period in which these studies have been written the majority of our great public libraries have been sorely depleted, by evacuation and by enemy action, particularly of the books to which I wished to refer. As a result of this, the greater part of the references are to books in my own possession or to those which I have borrowed from my friends; I have given my references in greater detail than might otherwise have been necessary, and where I have quoted from an edition later than the first, I have attempted to give the date of that in parentheses.

As these studies are historical rather than critical, I have preferred actual quotation to paraphrase wherever possible.

I hope I have expressed my thanks to all those who have helped me, in my notes, but I cannot forbear mentioning the especial kindness of my friends Geoffrey Keynes and Thomas Balston. My equal gratitude to two other friends is conveyed in the dedication.

Unrevised versions of these essays have appeared in Horizon, New Road 1944, New Road 1945 *and* The Windmill; *my acknowledgements are due to the editors of these collections and periodicals, and also my thanks for the loan of blocks.*

RUTHVEN TODD

TRACKS IN THE SNOW

'. . . The principles of these sciences, and a taste for books of natural history contributed to multiply my ideas and images; and the anatomist and chemist may sometimes track me in their own snow.'[1]

'Imagine two lines, two straight lines, one running through Isaac Newton, Hunter, Monboddo, and [Erasmus] Darwin, the other through William Law and the mystics. Between them the wavy line of romantic sensibility. The three lines intersect in a few great men.'[2]

With these two quotations as my text I propose to embark on a short voyage of discovery. When we look back at the thick and seemingly matted forest of English literature through which we have already passed, bewildered by the medley of trees our eyes are inclined to focus only on the main track, well beaten by the regular passage of the professorial chariot-wheels. If, by some odd chance, our eyes should wander towards some half-hidden and overgrown or tangled pathway, it is in search of an obscure or underrated author of poetry or literary prose that they do so and seldom to seek out the writer whose interests and works are primarily unconcerned with literary or æsthetic considerations. Generally, it can be said that we lack a proper curiosity about such a writer's influence when his small path comes up against the major way.

In the following notes, which connect almost enough quotations to make a small anthology, I hope to give some indication of the manner in which the work of the scientists of the seventeenth and eighteenth centuries impacted upon those who followed them and whose interests were more purely æsthetic.

If many of my examples are taken from the works of Christopher Smart, William Blake and John Clare, that is because I have not the knowledge to prepare a full-scale *Road to Xanadu*[3] for my period, and can only hope to draw a dotted and uncertain line across the face of a map, one of these indications of the possible or probable course of a river across a still unexplored and uncharted territory. Before I attempt to pencil in this wavering line I must first try to give the general outline of the map itself, though even that is ill-defined, full of strange bays and monstrous headlands.

By the middle of the seventeenth century thought had progressed from its blind acceptance of the Aristotelian concept, according to which the world was co-eternal with God, to an equally blind acceptance of the Scriptural view, which posited an eternal God performing an act of creation in the year 4004 B.C., a date firmly established by Bishop James Ussher and accepted beyond all possible question in England.[4]

Into this narrow framework of time all human history and all natural phenomena had to be fitted, trimmed and amputated or stretched and inflated. The problem of chronology had become very real and very immediate, so much so that a man of the stature of Sir Isaac Newton considered his scientific discoveries as feathers in the balance against the heavy gold of his theological and chronological works.[5] No longer could the words of the Bible be altered, or 'interpreted', by a Council of the Roman Church: all difficulties had to be solved by a direct reference to the unchangeable 'Word' itself and Tradition was excommunicated and exiled to live in sin upon the mountain-tops with the Whore of Babylon and her Apocalyptic nurslings.

Despite the restrictions of this intractable code, the punishments which followed the discovery of some unacceptable fact were no longer so various and severe as formerly they had been, but the desire to inquire into natural objects still had to be explained and justified

2. Joseph Wright. An Experiment with an Air-Pump

3. Pictorial Museum Exhibit

by the seeker. The influence of Francis Bacon was slowly filtering through the minds of those who had any pretensions to education, and the virus infected Sir Thomas Browne with the realization that 'The wisdom of God receives small honour from those vulgar Heads that rudely stare about, and with a gross rusticity admire his works; those highly magnifie him, whose judicious inquiry into his Acts, and deliberate research into his Creatures, return the duty of a devout and learned admiration.'[6]

In this world where the curious imagination had still to face the frowns of the religious brow, where the Puritan use of the Bible as a sort of combined *Pears' Encyclopædia* and Mrs. Emily Post on etiquette was to linger on for at least a couple of centuries; in this world of narrow boundaries and forbidden areas, it must have been comforting when a divine of the eminence of Bishop Thomas Burnet started exploring the past and pointed out that 'the obscurity of these things, and their remoteness from common knowledge will be made an argument by some, why we should not undertake them; and by others, it may be, the very same thing will be made an argument why we should; for my part I think *There is nothing so secret that shall not be brought to Light*, within the compass of *Our World*; for we are not to understand that of the whole Universe, nor of all Eternity, our capacities do not extend so far; But whatsoever concerns this Sublunary World in the whole extent of its duration, from the Chaos to the last period, this I believe Providence hath made us capable to understand, and will in its due time make it known. All I say, betwixt the first Chaos and the last Completion of Time and all things temporary, This was given to the disquisitions of men; On either hand is Eternity, before the world and after, which is without our reach: But that little spot of ground that lies betwixt those two great Oceans, this we are to cultivate, this we are Masters of, herein we are to exercise our Thoughts, to understand and lay open the treasures of the Divine Wisdom and Goodness hid in this part of Nature and of Providence.'[7]

When Thomas Sprat, Bishop of Rochester, wrote his *History of the Royal Society*, founded in 1660, he was forced to devote the whole of the first part to a history of 'natural philosophy' answering the objections of those who would condemn the 'philosopher' and his objective desire for experimental proof. In addition to rebuking those whose belief in Divine Revelation as the sole source of truth had led them into a state of intolerance, Sprat called to order that multitude of others whose lives were spent in unnecessary conflict over the finer points of religion: 'And now there comes into our View another remarkable Occasion of the Hindrance of the Growth of *Experimental Philosophy*, within the Compass of this bright Age; and that is the great a do which has been made, in raising, and confirming, and refuting so many different Sects, and opinions of the *Christian Faith*. For whatever other Hurt or Good comes by such holy speculative Wars (of which whether the Benefit or Mischief overweighs, I will not now examine) yet certainly by this means, the knowledge of Nature has been very much retarded. And (to use that Metaphor, which an excellent Poet of our Nation turns to another purpose) that Shower has done very much Injury by falling on the Sea, for which the Shepherd and the Plough-man call'd in vain; The Wit of Man has been profusely pour'd out on *Religion*, which needed not its help, and which was only thereby made more tempestuous; while it might have been more fruitfully spent, on some Parts of Philosophy, which have been hitherto barren, and might soon have been made fertile.'[8]

This was an age of acrimonious controversy, when one's opponent stood naked before the bayonet of the

4. Pictorial Museum Exhibit

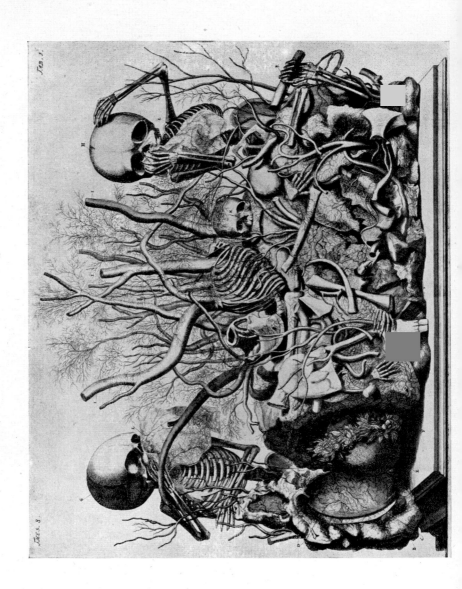

Tab. I.

unsheathed tongue and when wounds were rubbed in the bitter ink stewed, with green vitriol, from oak-galls and rusty nails. Among the whirling leaves of the pamphlets, and the thunder of John Milton damning bishops, it is not always easy to hear the quiet voice of tolerance: 'Although we are secured in fundamental points from involuntary errour, by the plaine, expresse, and dogmaticall places of Scripture, yet in other things we are not but may be invincibly mistaken, because of the obscurity and difficulty in the controverted parts of Scripture, by reason of the incertainty of the meanes of its Interpretation, since Tradition is of an uncertain reputation, and sometimes evidently false, Councels are contradictory to each other, and therefore certainly are equally deceiv'd many of them, and therefore all may; and then the Popes of Rome are very likely to mislead us, but cannot ascertain us of truth in matter of Question; and in this world we believe in part, and prophesy in part, and this imperfection shall never be done away till we be translated to a more glorious state; either we must throw our chances, and get truth by accident or predestination, or else we must lie safe in mutuall toleration, and private liberty of perswasion, unless some other Anchor can bee thought upon where wee may fasten our floating Vessels, and ride safely'. [9]

Despite all the pleas of tolerant or experimentally minded Bishops, the biblical ropes still attempted to hold the scientist tethered on his narrow green, cropping only known and cultivated varieties of plants. There was a general unwillingness to accept the state of affairs so well described by Sir William Cecil Dampier when he writes: 'It is evident that in the age of Newton—the age of the first great synthesis of scientific knowledge—the revolution in the intellectual outlook of mankind involved a revolution in the statement of dogmatic religious belief. On the one hand, it was impossible to continue to hold the naïve conception of the Cosmos which had become embedded in Aristotelian and Thomist philosophy, impossible any longer to gaze into heaven, just above the sky and to shudder at the rumblings of hell beneath the ground. Light ceased to be an all-pervading mysterious substance of colourless purity, the very dwelling-place of God, and became a physical manifestation, having laws to be investigated with mirrors and lenses, and colours to be analysed by a prism. On the other hand, the type of instinctive inarticulate Platonism which is seen in pietism and mysticism was equally inapplicable to the new mental attitude. Men were left with the more rational Platonism, which, like the first type, held that eternal truth is reached by an innate power or revelation from within, yet regarded mathematical or geometrical harmony as the essence of being. This variety of Platonism led through the ideas of Galileo and Kepler to the mathematical system of Newton. It accepted the inner power or revelation as the basis of reason, and the theory then became a form of intellectualism, which sought to find the truth about the Divine Nature both in the physical order of the Universe, and in the moral law.'[10]

Yet, when we come to examine the poets, we shall find that as a rule it was the 'enthusiastic' believer in revealed religion who integrated the words and the discoveries of the scientists into his own world, rather than the rational materialist writer of poems on science living in a mathematical universe, such as Abraham Cowley, whose poems are too often only examples of an up-to-date attitude, such as that of the Georgian poet who, in the early years of the twentieth century, wrote poems on motor-cars or airplanes.

To return now to my brief sketch of the historical background. Some idea of the difficulties under which the inquiring mind worked can be gained from the evidence of the great naturalist John Ray,[11] who wrote in his explanation of fossils: 'It will hence follow, that many Species of Animals have been lost out of the

World, which Philosophers and Divines are unwilling to admit, esteeming the Destruction of any one *Species* a Dismembring of the Universe, and rendring the World imperfect; whereas they think the Divine Providence is especially concerned, and solicitous to secure and preserve the Works of the Creation. And truly so it is, as appears, in that it was so careful to lodge all Land Animals in the Ark at the Time of the general Deluge; and in that, of all Animals recorded in Natural Histories, we cannot say that there hath been any one Species lost, no not of the most infirm, and most exposed to Injury and Ravine. Moreover, it is likely, that as there neither is nor can be any new Species of Animals produced, all proceeding from Seeds at first created; so Providence, without which one individual Sparrow falls not to the Ground, doth in that manner watch over all that are created, that an entire Species shall not be lost or destroyed by any Accident.' [12]

In justice to Ray it must at once be made clear that he firmly held that the 'most probable Opinion is that they were originally the Shells or Bones of living Fishes and other Animals bred in the sea', [13] and he managed to overcome the difficulty, raised by the theologians, that the admission of the fact of extinction was a criticism of the Divine Wisdom, by stating that 'there may be some of them remaining some where or other in the Seas, though as yet they have not come to my Knowledge. For though they may have perished, or by some Accident been destroyed out of our Seas, yet the Race of them may be preserved and continued still in others. So though Wolves and Bevers, which we are well assured were sometimes native of *England*, have been here utterly destroyed and extirpated out of this Island, yet there remain Plenty of them still in other Countries.' [14]

A little further reading of Ray's works shows that sometimes he could even manage to grasp the scriptural ropes to plait them to his own purpose, as in his rejection

of the commonly accepted theory of Spontaneous Generation, for 'Creation being the Work of Omnipotency, and
incommunicable to any Creature, it must be beyond the
Power of Nature or natural Agents, to produce things
after that manner. And as for God Almighty, He is said
to have rested from His Work of Creation after the
Seventh Day. But if there be any Spontaneous Generation,
there was nothing done at the Creation, but what is daily
done; for The Earth and Water produc'd Animals then
without Seed, and so they do still.'¹⁵

How late the prejudices against anything which seemed
to run counter to the direct word of the first chapter of
Genesis continued can be seen from the case of Dr.
William Buckland, Dean of Westminster, who published
his book on geology¹⁶ under the auspices of the Bridge-
water bequest, established in 1829, under terms very
similar to those of the Boyle lectures, to produce a series
of works 'On the Power, Wisdom, and Goodness of God,
as manifested in the Creation; illustrating such work by
all reasonable arguments, as for instance the variety and
formation of God's creatures in the animal, vegetable, and
mineral kingdoms; the effect of digestion, and thereby of
conversion; the construction of the hand of man, and an
infinite variety of other arguments; as also by discoveries
ancient and modern, in arts, sciences, and the whole extent
of literature'.¹⁷

Before he could settle down to his subject, Buckland
had to deal with possible criticism by showing that there
was no fundamental theological objection to his necessary
assumption that each 'day' in *Genesis* was, in fact, a
symbol for a very considerable period of time. Further,
he found it necessary to explain that 'The disappointment
of those who look for a detailed account of geological
phenomena in the Bible, rests on a gratuitous expectation
of finding therein historical information, respecting all
the operations of the Creator in times and places with

which the human race has no concern; as reasonably might we object that the Mosaic history is imperfect, because it makes no specific mention of the satellites of Jupiter, or the rings of Saturn, as feel disappointment at not finding in it the history of geological phenomena, the details of which may be fit matter for an encyclopædia of science, but are foreign to the objects of a volume intended only to be a guide of religious belief and moral conduct'.[18]

It is a long and involved journey from the apologetic tones of the seventeenth-century natural philosopher to the early nineteenth-century scientists' strictures upon Descartes, 'But in philosóphy he failed, his genius taking a wrong turn through the brilliancy of his imagination, which led him to invent systems of nature, instead of investigating her laws by means of judicious experiments, painfully and patiently pursued'.[19]

Yet between the apologists[20] and those who insisted upon experimentation as the proper duty of every right-minded man, there lies the country with the wonderful mine of bright and glittering ore, where the poets and artists could quarry to their hearts' content, knowing that even the pyrites and quartz they carried to the surface—gold and diamonds in the strange half-light underground—would attract an audience for whom the world was still an object small enough for them to cuddle in their hands like a bubble-glass of brandy.

How far, and into what unexpected quarters, the mining fever spread we know from the description of Dr. Johnson's garret in Gough Square where 'I observed an apparatus for chymical experiments, of which Johnson was all his life very fond'.[21] And even in the nineteenth century we find Thomas Lovell Beddoes, who had hoped to rob death of its horrors by his jokes, hopefully pursuing the ideal of the Philosopher's Stone, which in addition to its auriferous qualities was also reputed to be a kind of universal heal-all.[22]

The ghost of the Honourable Robert Boyle, 'the Father
of Chemistry and Uncle of the Earl of Cork' as the Irish
epitaph is said to call him,[23] stalks through the period
leaving an impress deeper than that left by the ghost of
the King in *Hamlet*. One of the supreme inquiring minds,
Boyle's interests were literally infinite. He rejected the
old idea of the four 'elements' and of the 'principles' of
salt, sulphur and mercury being the basis of all substances,
despite his own life-long preoccupation with alchemy.[24]
He collected hydrogen over water, studied the growth
and forms of crystals as a help towards understanding
chemical structure, and collected many facts about
electricity, magnetism, temperature and atmospheric
pressure. It was as a result of his insistence that John
Evelyn wrote his book on the art of engraving on copper,[25]
and at the end of the eighteenth century we find the
ingenious still repeating the experiments he tried with
his 'Pneumatical Engine', which he and Robert Hooke,
that ingenious mechanic, had improved from the air-
pump invented by von Guericke in 1654.

Before glancing at the appearance of the air-pump in
painting and literature, it would be well to look at some
of Boyle's own accounts of a few of his experiments:

'*Exp. I.*—August 16, 1670. A linnet being put into a
receiver, capable to hold about $4\frac{1}{2}$ pints of water, the glass
well closed with cement and a cover; but none of the air
was drawn out with the engine or otherwise. And though
no new air was let in, nor any change made to the
imprisoned air, yet the bird continued there three hours
without any apparent approach to death; and though it
seemed somewhat sick, yet being afterwards taken out,
it recovered and lived several hours.

'*Exp. II.*—Aug. 18. From the above mentioned receiver
about half the air was drawn out, a linnet being then in the
glass, and in that rarefied air, which appeared by a gauge

to continue in that state, the bird lived an hour and a quarter before it seemed in danger of death; after which the air being let in without taking off the receiver, she manifestly recovered, and leaped against the side of the glass; being then taken out into the open air she flew out of my hand to a considerable distance.

'*Exp. III.*—Sept. 9. We conveyed into a receiver, capable of holding about $4\frac{1}{2}$ pints of water, a lark, together with the gauge, by the help whereof we pumped out of the receiver $\frac{3}{4}$ of the air that was in it before; then heedfully observing the bird, we perceived it pant very much, so that a learned physician (from whom I yet dissented), judged those beatings to be convulsive; having continued thus for a little more than a minute and a half; the bird fell into a true convulsive motion, that cast it upon the back. And although we made great haste to let in the air, yet before the expiration of the second minute, and consequently in less than half a minute from the time immediately preceding the convulsion, the lark was gone past all recovery, though divers means were used to effect it.' [26]

On page 12 is the scientist's view of his work, but when Joseph Wright of Derby, familiarized with 'experimental philosophy' by his friendship with the eccentric and inquiring Erasmus Darwin, [27] chose the course of an experiment, like the third described by Boyle, as the subject for one of his celebrated candle-light pictures, the scene became a dramatic situation, with the pathetic emotion heightened by a boy drawing up the empty cage on a pulley and the older of the two little girls weeping as she is told that the outcome of the experiment will be the death of the white-breasted bird fluttering in the glass globe. [28]

Though when he was offered the first number of the *Mechanic's Magazine* in 1823, William Blake declined it, with the remark, 'These things we artists HATE!', [29] thereby demonstrating his mistrust of the mechanist

conception of the universe derived from Bacon and Newton
(for 'Cowper came to me and said: "O that I were insane
always. I will never rest. Can you not make me truly insane?
I will never rest till I am so. O that in the bosom of God I
was hid. You retain health and yet are as mad as any of us
all—over us all—mad as a refuge from unbelief—from
Bacon, Newton and Locke" ' [30]); yet when he wished to be
satirical, he showed that he too lived in a world of ingenious
ladies and gentlemen, a world where a social evening
was devoted to 'globes, telescopes, microscopes, electrical
machines, air pumps, air guns, *a good bottle of wine*, and
other philosophical instruments'.[31] In the following quotation he shows his familiarity with the scientific experiments
of the time, particularly in his reference to plogiston, the
principle of fire, which was christened by G. E. Stahl and
which was supposed to possess negative weight, for the
experiments of Boyle and others had shown that when
metals were burned the solid increased in weight. It seems
probable that the reference here is to Joseph Priestley, who
prepared oxygen by heating mercuric oxide and, failing to
recognize the importance or true nature of his discovery,
called it 'dephlogisticated air'.[32]

'But felicity does not last long, for being met at the
house of Inflammable Gass the windfinder, the following
affairs happen'd.

'"Come, Flammable," said Gibble Gabble, "& let's
enjoy ourselves. Bring the Puppets."

'"Hay,—Hay," said he, "you—sho—why—ya, ya.
How can you be so foolish? Ha! Ha! Ha! She calls the
experiments puppets!"

'Then he went upstairs & loaded the maid with glasses,
& brass tubes & magic pictures.

'"Here, ladies & gentlemen," said he, "I'll shew
you a louse, or a flea, or a butterfly, or a cockchafer, the
blade bone of a tittle-back. No, no. Here's a bottle of wind

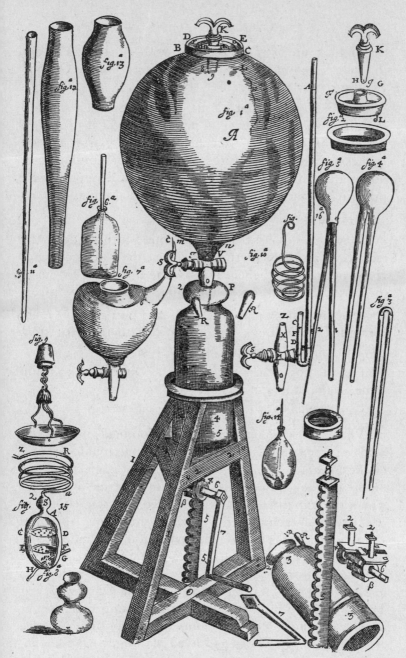

Robert Boyle's Air-Pump. From *Nova Experimenta Physico-Mechanica de vi aëris elastica*, Geneva, 1680.

that I took up in the boghouse, and—O dear, O dear, the water's got into the sliders! Look here, Gibble Gabble! Lend me your handkerchief, Tilly Lally.''

'Tilly Lally took out his handkerchief, which smear'd the glass worse than ever. Then he screw'd it on. Then he took the sliders, & then he set-up the glasses for the Ladies to view the pictures. Thus he was employ'd, & quite out of breath. While Tilly Lally & Scopprell were pumping at the air-pump, Smack went the glass.[33]

'"Hang!" said Tilly Lally.

'Inflammable Gass turn'd short round & threw down the table & Glasses, & Pictures, & broke the bottles of wind, & let out the Pestilence. He saw the Pestilence fly out of the bottle, & cried out, while he ran out of the room:

'"Come out! Come out! We are putrified! We are corrupted! Our lungs are destroy'd with the Flogiston. This will spread a plague all thro' the Island!"

'He was downstairs the very first. On the back of him came all the others in a heap.

'So they need not bidding go.'[34]

When Christopher Smart was confined in Bedlam between 1758 and 1763 and wrote his long hymn of praise to the Creator, *Jubilate Agno*, he did not neglect the air-pump and he showed his knowledge of the difficulties which the experimenters encountered in their efforts to create a total vacuum, efforts which must have appeared almost sacrilegious to the Aristotelian mind, founded upon the belief that nature abhorred a vacuum. The direct source of Smart's information on the subject of the air-pump was undoubtedly the lectures delivered in the Observatory at Trinity College by that extraordinary young man, Roger Cotes, of whom Newton himself is reported to have observed, 'If Mr. Cotes had lived we might have known something'.[35] These lectures were started by William

Whiston and, after Cotes's death they were continued, and
published, by his successor, Robert Smith. In his lectures
and demonstrations Cotes showed that the air was removed
from the receiver of the air-pump in perpetually diminish-
ing quantities which he worked out mathematically. His
principal point was formulated in his statement that 'you
may approach as near as you please to a perfect vacuum.
But notwithstanding this, you can never entirely take
away the remainder.'[36] No doubt the implications Smart
managed to give the engine would have astonished Boyle,
though he himself had considered all his work to be to the
greater glory of God, for as a scientist he had been content
to work, noting down his results and adding to the sum
of human knowledge, without much immediate concern
about their theological repercussions:

'For the AIR-PUMP weakens & dispirits but cannot
wholly exhaust.

'For SUCKTION is the withdrawing of life, but life
will follow as fast as it can.

'For there is infinite provision to keep up the life in all
parts of Creation.'[37]

It is obvious in this passage that Smart is trying to
reconcile the achievement of an almost complete vacuum
with the ideas, generally accepted as propounded by Ray
in the quotations already given, that a Benevolent Creator
could not countenance the complete extinction of any
sort of life.

How much later the air-pump remained a part of the
life of the curious, we can see from the description of
Shelley's room at Oxford where 'An electrical machine, an
air-pump, the galvanic trough, a solar microscope, and
large glass jars and receivers, were conspicuous amidst the
mass of matter'.[38]

In the remarkable and most important poem already
mentioned, Christopher Smart ranged through his life's

reading, calling upon all nature from the biblical palmer-worm and practically the whole of Pliny to 'the Great Flabber Dabber Flat Clapping Fish with hands' [39] to praise the Lord and magnify him for ever. That, in addition to the books mentioned by the editor of the poem, Smart was also familiar with the lectures of Roger Cotes, to which reference has already been made, cannot, I think, be doubted, for a large part of Section IX seems to derive directly from passages in them, particularly the parts dealing with Capillary Tubes, Mercury and the Barometer.

He shows, moreover, that he was familiar with the various theories propounded to explain the existence of fossils, as listed in John Ray's *Observations made in a Journey through part of the Low Countries* and *Three Physico-Theological Discourses*:

'Let Syntche rejoice with Myax—There are shells in the earth which were left by the FLOOD.

'Let Clement rejoice with Ophidon—There are shell again in earth at sympathy with those in sea.

'Let Epaphroditus rejoice with Ophthalmias—The Lord increase the Cambridge collection of fossils.' [40]

While at Pembroke, Smart had no doubt frequently seen the large collection of fossils formed by John Woodward and bequeathed by him to the University in 1728, but it is clear that in his tortured mind the fossil had become a symbol not only of the Deluge but also of the universality and unity of life.

Blake makes no direct reference to fossils, although *Vala, or the Four Zoas* and *Jerusalem* are full of references to petrification which may, of course, be Biblical in their derivation, as in the story of Lot's wife. However, it would be absurd to suggest that he did not know of the speculation current at his time for, according to Gideon Mantell, his friend George Cumberland was 'a celebrated geologist', [41] and the subject must have been discussed by them.

One subject of common speculation which seems to have impressed Smart particularly still sometimes turns up in the columns of local newspapers. This is the story of the living toad completely imprisoned in the centre of a piece of wood or stone. To this legend, Ray, impressed by the weight of apparently unimpeachable evidence, devoted considerable attention, seeking to explain it in some way that his eminently reasonable mind could accept, without having recourse to the impossible theory of Spontaneous Generation. He wrote: 'Those Animals, when young and little, finding in the stone some small Hole reaching to the middle of it, might, as their Nature is, creep into it, as a fit *Latibulum* for the Winter, and there grow too big to return back by the Passage by which they enter'd and so continue imprisoned therein for many years; a little Air, by reason of the Coldness of the Creature, and its lying torpid there sufficing it for Respiration, and the Humour of the Stone, by reason it lay immovable, and spent not, for Nourishment. And I do believe, that if those who found such Toads, had diligently searched, they might have discovered, and traced the way whereby they enter'd in, or some Footsteps of it. Or else there might fall down into the lapideous Matter before it was concrete into a Stone some small Toad, (or some Toad Spawn) which being not able to extricate itself and get out again, might remain there imprisoned till the Matter about it were condensed and compacted into a Stone.' [42]

The truth of the story was finally shown to be not too far removed from Ray's common-sense explanation by Dean Buckland's experiments in sealing toads up in cells in apple-trees, limestone, sandstone and of plaster-of-paris. These experiments ended in the deaths of the unfortunate creatures. [43]

For Christopher Smart, however, the toad shut away from the glories of the world became identified with himself shut in Bedlam (a point which is made clear by the

second of my quotations). As a reward for the close con-
finement and the dullness of his prison, the toad, possessor
of a wonderful jewel hidden in his head—again we have
the connection with Smart—was to inherit more of the
kingdom of heaven than others might have allotted to it:

'For a TOAD can dwell in the centre of a stone,
because there are stones whose constituent life is of
these creatures.

'For a Toad hath by means of his eye the most beautiful
prospects of any other animal to make him amends for his
distance from his Creator in Glory . . .'[44]

'For a toad enjoys a finer prospect than another
creature to compensate his lack.

> Tho' toad I am the object of man's hate
> Yet better am I than a reprobate,
>   who has the worst of prospects . . .'[45]

'For there are stones, whose constituent particles are
little toads.'[46]

John Clare, also, beset with debts, the fear of witches,
and the feeling that he had been deserted by his friends,
turned in a poem written about 1832 which seems to forecast his removal, nearly ten years later, to the Northampton
General Lunatic Asylum, to the same painful image:

> 'To be and not to be and still to know it,
> Like toad, life-buried in the solid rock,
> Were a blest lot and happiness to mine,
> Possessed of feelings that burn out the mind,
> Like to a candle snuff, . . .'[47]

That Clare was familiar with John Ray we know from
his own earlier words,

> 'Nay, had I Darwin's prying thought,
> Or all the learning Ray has taught,

> How soon description would exhaust,
> And in sweet Flora's lap be lost . . . '[11]

and his remarks about Linnæus, that 'Modern works are so mystified by systematic symbols that one cannot understand them till the wrong end of one's life-time; and when one turns to the works of Ray, Parkinson, and Gerard, where there is more of nature and less of art, it is like meeting the fresh air and balmy summer of a dewy morning after the troubled dreams of a nightmare'.[49]

Thus, for both Christopher Smart and John Clare, the toad, derived from their reading, for I do not think Clare refers to it in his letters on nature, became a personal symbol, to be envied either on account of its enforced life-long solitude or for its future happiness. Incidentally, it is interesting to note that the same legend was applied, though not so commonly, to the newt, and that Blake may refer to this at the end of *Vala, or the Four Zoas* when he writes

> 'The scaly newt creeps
> From the stone.'[50]

It would be going rather far to suggest that when Blake wrote

> 'To see a World in a Grain of Sand
> And a Heaven in a Wild Flower,
> Hold infinity in the palm of your hand
> And Eternity in an hour.'[15]

and

> 'In particles bright
> The jewels of Light
> Distinct shone & clear.
> Amaz'd & in fear
> I each particle gazed,
> Astonish'd, Amazed;
> For each was a Man
> Human-form'd . . .'[52]

there was any direct connection with the following passage, from John Ray, but it is clear that his microcosmic view could not have existed without the microscopic work of scientists like Antony van Leeuwenhoek and Robert Hooke.

'Our sight doth not give us the just Magnitude of Things, but only their Proportion; and what appears to the Eye as a Point, may be magnified so, even by Glasses as to discover an incredible Multitude of Parts; nay, some Animals there are, so small, that if a Grain of Sand were broken into 8,000,000 of equal Parts, one of these would not exceed the biggness of one of those Creatures, as Mr. *Lewenhoek* affirms. And Dr. *Hook* proceeds farther, and says, that he had discovered some so exceedingly small, that Millions of Millions might be contained in one Drop of Water. If these whole Creatures be so incredibly little, what shall we think of their Parts containing and contained, their Entrails and Muscles, their Ovaries and Eggs? . . . the Unconceivable, I had almost said Infinite, Divisibility of Matter . . .' [53]

That Smart also at times subscribed to this microscopic point of view we can see from the last quotation on the subject of toads, given above.

The point I set out to make, that the writer drew largely from the writings of the scientist, transforming his plunder for his own ends, should now be fairly obvious, but that the trade was not entirely one-way is equally true. To show how the artist's influence worked, here is a description of an exhibit from Frederik Ruysch's anatomical museum at Amsterdam, round about 1700: 'No serious attempt is made towards a scientific classification of animals or organs, or to build up a system of philosophic anatomy. In place of this the preparations are arranged, not to illustrate any principle of biological science, but to produce a picturesque effect. A skeleton balances an injected spermatic plexus in one hand and a coil of viscera in the other; minatory assortments of

6. Pictorial Museum Exhibit

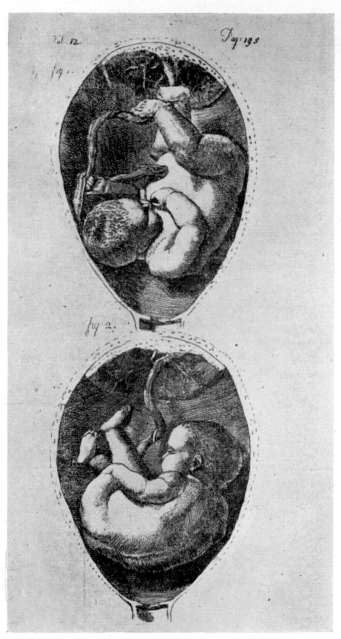

7. GEORGE STUBBS. Embryos

calculi of all sizes and shapes occupy the foreground; in the rear a variety of injected vessels backed by an inflated and injected tunica vaginalis combine to form a grotesque arboreal perspective; another skeleton *in extremis* is grasping a specimen of that emblem of insect mortality, the mayfly, and a third is performing a composition "expressing the sorrows of mankind" on a violin symbolized by a bundle of injected arteries and a fragment of necrotic femur. Bones are arranged to represent a cemetery, wrists are adorned with organic and injected frills, and human, comparative and pathological exhibits are indiscriminately mingled as the exigencies of space required. Of those vast philosophic conceptions which discriminate the Hunterian collection, no suggestion can be traced. Instead of the joy and stimulus of scientific speculation, the museum only reminds him [the student] of the sorrows of this world and the perils of the next. Quotations from the Latin Poets of a gloomy and despairing nature, insistent in big type, inspire the hope that the diffusion of the Latin tongue was more restricted than it is today. "Ab utero ad tumultum", "communis ad lethum via", "ah fata, ah aspera fata", are examples of the cheerful subjects for moral reflection which restrained the levity of the mediæval student; and "mundus lachrymarum vallis" was considered an appropriate introduction to the skeleton of a woman.'[54]

As the eighteenth century progressed it became increasingly clear that in a world which had become the mathematical projection of a mathematical God, the natural conclusion which was drawn from the works of Descartes, Boyle, Newton and Locke, the gathering of unrelated information with the intention of showing the wisdom of God in the creation, as exemplified by the physico-theological writers, Ray and Derham,[55] had to give way before the more ambitious philosophical systems, such as those created by John Hunter in his collection

c

and Linnæus with his system of the classification of plants by their sex organs. Where John Ray stands out apart from the other physico-theologians is that he realized the necessity of a system and his attempts at classification have, in the light of evolution, come to be accepted as the basis of the system used today.

The point of view of the late eighteenth century was well expressed by the still under-estimated Erasmus Darwin, in the preface to his *Zoonomia*, when he wrote, 'The great CREATOR of all things has infinitely diversified the works of his hands, but has at the same time stamped a certain similitude on the features of nature, that demonstrates to us, that *the whole is one family of one parent*'.[56] As the nineteenth century progressed the increasing concentration upon detail placed the grasp of the whole outside the comprehensions of all save a very few exceptional minds, so that the specialist came into his own and the amateur vanished from the scene, and we no longer find a portrait painter like Benjamin Wilson as a Fellow of the Royal Society, contributing papers on electricity to the *Philosophical Transactions*.

To finish this short glance at the subject there is the figure of George Stubbs 'whose vision was the scientific vision'[57] and who devoted his life to an unending study of anatomy. At the age of eight he is said to have borrowed 'bones and prepared subjects'[58] from a neighbouring doctor, and before he was twenty-two he was lecturing on anatomy to medical students in York. It was at York that he met Dr. John Burton, who appears in *Tristram Shandy* as Dr. Slop and who is also memorable as the inventor of one of the earlier patterns of obstetric forcep.[59] Working on the body of a woman, taken from the grave by his students, and upon other material, Stubbs made the dissections which he etched himself in Burton's *A New and Complete System of Midwifery*, 1751. That Burton was pleased with the illustrations we can see from his

justification of their inclusion in his book, 'Some incon-
siderate People look upon *Copper-Plates*, in this Case,
to be useless; but judicious Persons must be sensible,
that in describing Objects not to be seen, the Reader
will have a better Idea of them from a true Representation
upon a *Plate*, than only from a bare Description, as is
evident in all Branches of *Philosophy*'.[60]

After a brief visit to Italy, Stubbs settled at Horkstow
and, hanging dead horses from hooks in the kitchen
rafters, set to work on the book by which he is still best
remembered, *The Anatomy of the Horse*,[61] injecting veins
and viscera with all the enthusiasm of Ruysch preparing
an exhibit for his museum. When the book was published
its success was not confined to country gentlemen and
artists, but reached also into the scientific world. It was
highly praised by the anatomists, Albrecht von Haller
and Petrus Camper, and, more especially, it brought the
artist the friendship of John Hunter.

Professor Cole says: 'John Hunter's conception of
comparative anatomy accepts man as the central object,
with whom other types are to be compared. Therefore
the human body must be mastered first, for if we do not
understand the standard we cannot expect to understand
the variations from it',[62] and there can be no doubt that
it was his friend's influence, and his desire to build up a
comprehensive system, which influenced Stubbs in the
choice of subject for his great unfinished work, *The
Comparative Anatomical Exposition of the Structure of the
Human Body, with that of a Tiger and a Common Fowl*.[63]
In this work Stubbs showed not only his mastery as a
draughtsman and engraver, but also the closeness of his
connection with the ideas of the time, which were meeting
the demands of Sir Thomas Browne, who, as an exponent
of Baconian ideals, declared that, so far as his work was
concerned, he would 'only take notice of such, whose
experimentall and judicious knowledge shall solemnly

looke upon it; not onely to destroy of ours, but to establish of his owne, not to traduce or extenuate, but to explaine, and dilucidate, to adde and ampliate, according to the laudable custome of the Ancients in their sober promotions of Learning'.[64]

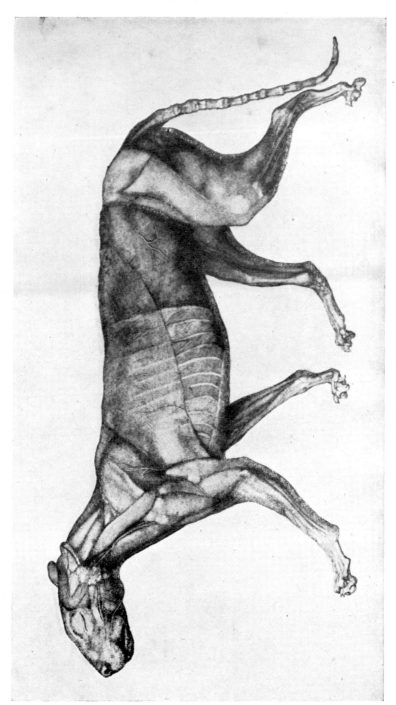

8. GEORGE STUBBS. Tiger

Tab. x

9. GEORGE STUBBS. Common Fowl

REFERENCES

1 *The Memoirs of Edward Gibbon by Himself*, ed. George Birkbeck Hill, London, 1900, p. 201. [1796 & 1814.]

2 Geoffrey Grigson, *The Romantics*, London, 1942, p. 339.

3 Professor John Livingston Lowes's study of the sources of *The Rime of the Ancient Mariner* and *Kubla Khan*, London, 1927, revised 1930.

4 For Ussher's chronology see *Annales Veteris et Novi Testamenti*, 2 vols., London, 1650–4, translated by Thomas Fuller and others, 1658.

5 Sir Isaac Newton, *The Chronology of Ancient Kingdoms amended*, London, 1728; see also Louis Trenchard More, *Isaac Newton*, New York and London, 1934.

6 *Religio Medici*, p. 7, *The Works of the Learned Sir Thomas Browne, Kt.*, London, 1686. [*Religio Medici*, 1642, first authorized ed. 1643.]

7 *The Theory of the Earth: Containing an Account of the Original of the Earth, and of all the General Changes Which it hath already undergone, Or is To Undergo, Till the Consummation of all Things*, London, 1684–90, i, 5. [Latin ed. 1681–9.]

8 *The History of the Royal Society of London, for the Improving of Natural Knowledge*, The Third Edition Corrected, London, 1722, pp. 25–6. [1667.]

9 ΘΕΟΛΟΓΙΑ ΕΚΛΕΚΤΙΚΗ, *A Discourse of the Liberty of Prophesying, shewing The Unreasonableness of Prescribing to other mens Faith, and the Iniquity of persecuting differing opinions*, Jeremy Taylor, London, 1647, pp. 150–1.

10 *A History of Science and its relations with Philosophy and Religion*, Third Edition, Cambridge, 1942, pp. 190–1. [1929.]

11 See *John Ray, Naturalist, His Life and Works*, Charles E. Raven, D.D., Cambridge, 1942; an outstanding biography.

12 *Three Physico-Theological Discourses Concerning I. The Primitive Chaos, and Creation of the World. II. The General Deluge, its Causes and Effects. III. The Dissolution of the World and Future Conflagration*, The Third Edition, London, 1713, pp. 172–3. [1692.]

[13] *Observations Topographical, Moral, & Physiological; Made in a Journey Through part of the Low Countries,* London, 1673, p. 120.

[14] *Three Physico-Theological Discourses, ed. cit.,* pp. 173-4.

[15] *The Wisdom of God Manifested in the Works of the Creation,* The Sixth Edition, Corrected, London, 1714, p. 300. [1691.]

[16] *Geology and Mineralogy considered with Reference to Natural Theology,* 2 vols., London, 1836.

[17] *Ibid.,* i, x.

[18] *Ibid.,* i, 14-15.

[19] *The Philosophical Transactions of the Royal Society of London, From their commencement in 1665, to the Year 1800; Abridged,* ed. Charles Hutton, George Shaw and Richard Pearson, London, 1809, i, 148 *note.*

[20] One of the best of these is Robert Boyle, *Some Considerations Touching the Usefulnesse of Experimental Natural Philosophy,* Oxford, 1663.

[21] *Boswell's Life of Johnson,* ed. George Birkbeck Hill, revised and enlarged L. F. Powell, Oxford, 1934, i, 436. [1791.]

[22] See H. W. Donner, *Thomas Lovell Beddoes, The Making of a Poet,* Oxford, 1935.

[23] *A History of Science, ed. cit.,* p. 152.

[24] See Louis Trenchard More, *The Life and Works of The Honorable Robert Boyle,* London and New York, 1944, XI, *Boyle as Alchemist.*

[25] *Sculptura: or the History, and Art of Chalcography and Engraving in Copper,* London, 1662.

[26] *Philosophical Transactions,* 1670, v, 63, p. 2026, quoted from *Phil. Trans. Abstracted, ed. cit.,* i, 491.

[27] See William Bemrose, *The Life and Works of Joseph Wright, A.R.A.,* London and Derby, 1885.

[28] The original painting is now in the possession of the Tate Gallery, on loan to Derby Art Gallery; my reproduction is of the mezzotint by Valentine Green, very kindly lent me by Mr. A. Reader, Charing Cross Road, London, W.C.2.

[29] Alexander Gilchrist, *Life of William Blake,* ed. Ruthven Todd, London and New York, 1942, p. 325. [1863, 1880.]

30 *The Poetry and Prose of William Blake*, ed. Geoffrey Keynes, London, 1939 ed., p. 817. Note written *c.* 1819 in Spurzheim, *Observations on the Deranged Manifestations of the Mind*, 1817.

31 *Memoirs of the First Forty-Five Years of the Life of James Lackington, Bookseller, Written by Himself*, Eighth Edition, London, 1794, p. 233. [1791.]

32 *A History of Science, ed. cit.*, pp. 197–8.

33 A common accident in Boyle's own experiments.

34 Blake, *ed. cit.*, pp. 686–7. *An Island in the Moon*, Chap. 10, written *c.* 1784.

35 More, *Newton*, p. 526. Newton's remark may have been prompted by gratitude for Cotes's work on the second edition of the *Principia*.

36 Roger Cotes, *Hydrostatical and Pneumatical Lectures*, ed. Robert Smith, London, 1738, p. 142.

37 *Rejoice in the Lamb, A Song from Bedlam*, ed. William Force Stead, London, 1939, ¶ IX, p. 87.

38 Thomas Jefferson Hogg, *Life of Shelley*, London, 1858, p. 169. For a discussion of Shelley's connections with science see Carl Grabo, *A Newton among Poets*, Chapel Hill, 1930.

39 *Jubilate Agno*, ¶ XXV, p. 157. Mr. Stead suggests that Smart has combined a phrase from *Psalm* xcviii with another from Anson's *Voyage*, 1748.

40 *Ibid.*, ¶ XIV, p. 111.

41 *The Journal of Gideon Mantell, Surgeon and Geologist*, ed. E. Cecil Curwen, London and New York, 1940, p. 2.

42 *The Wisdom of God, ed. cit.*, pp. 323–4. Mr. Stead draws attention to this passage in his notes to *Jubilate Agno*.

43 A full account of these experiments is given by his son, Francis T. Buckland, *Curiosities of Natural History*, 4 vols., The Popular Edition, London, 1883, i, 46–55. [1857.]

44 *Jubilate Agno*, ¶ XV, p. 113.

45 *Ibid.*, ¶ XVII, p. 124.

46 *Ibid.*, ¶ XVIII, p. 125.

47 T. W. and Anne Tibble, *John Clare, A Life*, London, 1932, pp. 370–1.

[48] *Ibid.*, p. 40.

[49] *Ibid.*, p. 87.

[50] Blake, *ed. cit.*, p. 364.

[51] Blake, *ed. cit.*, p. 118. *Auguries of Innocence.*

[52] Blake, *ed. cit.*, p. 846. Letter to Thomas Butts, 2 October 1804.

[53] *Three Physico-Theological Discourses, ed. cit.*, pp. 50–1.

[54] F. J. Cole, *A History of Comparative Anatomy from Aristotle to the Eighteenth Century*, London, 1944, pp. 458–60. I am indebted to Professor Cole for the very kind loan of a photograph of the engraving of the exhibit he describes in his fascinating book. Another plate, similar in subject and design, is reproduced by Douglas Guthrie, *A History of Medicine*, London, etc., 1945, pl. xxxix; I reproduce this, and a third, from loose prints in my possession.

[55] See W. Derham, *Physico-Theology: Or, A Demonstration of the Being and Attributes of God, from his Works of Creation*, London, 1713; Boyle Lectures, 1711–12.

[56] *Zoonomia; or, the Laws of Organic Life*, The Second Edition, Corrected, London, 1796, i, 1. [1794.]

[57] *George Stubbs*, 1724–1806, Geoffrey Grigson, *Signature*, London, 13, January 1940; the only attempt to consider Stubbs seriously.

[58] Joseph Mayer, *Memoirs of Thomas Dodd, William Upcott and George Stubbs, R.A.*, Liverpool, 1879, p. 5; Mr. Grigson points out, *loc. cit.*, that this memoir of Stubbs is founded upon notes by Ozias Humphry and not by William Upcott, as Mayer states.

[59] See Guthrie, *op. cit.*, pl. 1.

[60] *A New and Complete System of Midwifery, Theoretical and Practical*, The Second Edition, London, 1758, pp. xvii-xviii.

[61] London, 1766; facsimile with a modern paraphrase by Professor J. C. McCunn and C. W. Ottaway, London, 1938.

[62] Cole, *op. cit.*, p. 21.

[63] Subscribers' plates distributed 1804; uncompleted work published, London, 1817.

[64] *Pseudodoxia Epidemica: or, Enquiries into Very many received Tenents, And commonly presumed Truths*, London, 1646, *To the Reader.*

WILLIAM BLAKE AND THE
EIGHTEENTH-CENTURY
MYTHOLOGISTS

'MR. B. has done as all the ancients did, and as all the moderns who are worthy of fame, given the historical fact in it poetical vigour so as it always happens, and not in the dull way that some Historians pretend, who, being weakly organized themselves, cannot see either miracle or prodigy; all is to them a dull round of probabilities and possibilities; but the history of all times and places is nothing else but improbabilities and impossibilities; what we should say was impossible if we did not see it always before our eyes.'[1]

Any reader of English poetry before about 1830 must have been impressed and bewildered by the appearance of strange systems of mythology, systems which would appear to have no connection with the mythology which we know and which we have learned from our own teachers. In the following notes I can only hope to embroider the fringe of the subject so far as it concerns William Blake, and to do this I have attempted to renew the study of some of the books which we know him to have read and of these with which we have good reason for supposing him to have been familiar.

A horde of commentators has sought the explanation of the mystical elements expressed by Blake in his didactic writings, casting light into dark places with the aid of the torches of Paracelsus, Boehme, William Law and Swedenborg, but the speculative mythological background seems to have escaped the notice of all, with the partial exception of M. Denis Saurat.[2]

Before starting to examine these influences and their effects upon Blake's work, we have to realize, in making a study of his knowledge of any subject, that his approach was that of the eighteenth century, and of the eighteenth-century eclectic and inquiring mind. This was the attitude of mind which, even after it had discarded certain of the theories of the physico-theologists, approached the question of evolution from the angle of the ideas outlined by Erasmus Darwin and propounded by Jean Baptiste Lamarck, ideas which ruled that 'the effects of use and disuse and of environmental influences were supposed to be in some degree inherited',[3] so that we, our Darwinism with its dominant flavour of natural selection tinctured to some extent by the biological discoveries in gene-mutation of the geneticists, step immediately into another and quite unfamiliar world.

Further, it must be said that the Biblical story of the creation of man in all perfection as *Homo sapiens*, possessing 'his erect countenance, and his capacity for sublime contemplation',[4] was generally accepted as a matter of literal truth, together with a Biblical chronology which dated the creation of the world from four thousand and four years before the birth of Christ.

In the course of efforts to satisfy these irrevocable principles it was small wonder that the myth was not looked upon as an attempt to explain or justify the mysterious forces of nature, but rather as a method of recording history in a way that would impress it firmly upon the memories of all who heard it recounted, with the historian as poet engaged in the making of 'memorable speech'.[5]

The euhemerist approach to mythology, considering it as history, presented in a distorted and involved but ultimately comprehensible form, is of considerable antiquity, and, in England, nearly all the seventeenth-century theological and scientific authors seem to have indulged in it to a greater or lesser degree, for it was an urgent necessity to explain away any inconsistencies in the creation of a system of chronology. However, the efforts at correlation did not reach their peak until nearly three-quarters of the way through the eighteenth century, with the publication of the monumental work of the credulous Jacob Bryant,[6] who moved through the forest of speculation like a travelling sawmill, uprooting trees with a haphazard and happy disregard for their species so long as they could, by any possible means, be milled to fulfil his own preconceived specifications.

The best possible account of Bryant's methods and aims is that given by himself in his preface:

'As it will be my business to abridge history of every thing superfluous and foreign; I shall be obliged to set aside many ancient lawgivers, and princes, who were supposed to have formed republics, and to have founded kingdoms. I cannot acquiesce in the stale legends of Deucalion of Thessaly, of Inachus of Argos, and Ægialus of Sicyon: nor in the long line of princes, who are derived from them. The supposed heroes of the first ages in every country were equally fabulous. No such conquests were ever achieved, as are ascribed to Osiris, Dionysus, and Sesostris. The histories of Hercules, and Perseus, are equally void of truth. I am convinced, and hope I shall satisfactorily prove, that Cadmus never brought letters to Greece: and that no such person existed as the Grecians have described. What I have said about Sesostris and Osiris, will be repeated about Ninus, and Semiramis, two personages, as ideal as the former. There never were such expeditions undertaken, nor conquests made, as are attributed to these princes: nor were any such empires constituted, as are supposed to have been established by them. I make as little account of the histories of Saturn, Janus, Pelops, Atlas, Dardanus, Minos of Crete, and Zoroaster of Bactria. Yet something mysterious, and of moment, is concealed under these various characters; and the investigation of this latent truth will be the principle part of my inquiry. In respect to Greece, I can afford credence to very few events, which were antecedent to the Olympiads. I cannot give the least assent to the story of Phryxus, and the golden fleece. It seems to me plain beyond doubt, that there were no such persons as the Grecian Argonauts: and that the expedition of Jason to Colchis was a fable.

'After having cleared my way, I shall proceed to the sources, from whence the Grecians drew. I shall give an account of the Titans, and Titanic War, with the history of the Cuthites and ancient Babylonians. This will be accompanied with the Gentile history of the Deluge, the migration of mankind from Shinar, and the dispersion from Babel. The whole will be crowned with an account of ancient Egypt; wherein many circumstances of high consequence in chronology will be stated. In the execution of the whole there will be brought many surprizing proofs in confirmation of the Mosaic account: and it will be found from repeated evidence, that every thing, which the divine historian has transmitted, is most assuredly true. And though the nations, who preserved memorials of the deluge, have not perhaps stated accurately the time of that event; yet it will be found the grand epocha, to which they referred; the highest point, to which they could ascend. This was esteemed the renewal of the world; the new birth of mankind; and the ultimate of Gentile history.'[7]

The telescoping of history by the 'established' Biblical chronology justifies Bryant in his repudiation of the French historian, Joseph Juste Scaliger, who dealt with a period which exceeded 'the aera of the Mosaic creation 1336 years'.[8] Previous to the establishment and acceptance of the Darwinian explanation of the evolution of man and of an adequate and comprehensive system of philology, nothing can have appeared more reasonable and, indeed, more correct than Bryant's views with their attendant theory of a general hieroglyphic system preceding the invention of writing, views which, it must be remembered, were completely in keeping with all approved Scriptural teaching.

10. WILLIAM BLAKE. The Spiritual Form of Nelson

11. WILLIAM BLAKE. The Spiritual Form of Pitt

How widely these views were actually accepted can be seen from the evidence of the intelligent and inquiring Dr. Erasmus Darwin, who notes that 'There is an antient gem representing Venus rising out of the ocean supported by two Tritons. From the formality of the design it would appear to be of great antiquity before the introduction of fine taste into the world. It is probable that this beautiful allegory was originally an hieroglyphic picture (before the invention of letters) descriptive of the formation of the earth from the ocean, which seems to have been an opinion of many of the most antient philosophers.'[9]

Additional evidence of Bryant's influence, particularly of his low opinion of the Greeks, is provided by Sir William Chambers, Professor of Architecture at the Royal Academy, who denied that the Greeks had done anything which the Egyptians had not done before them, refusing them even the credit of the invention or establishment of the classical orders.[10]

The principal difficulty in allowing a separate and distinct source to each myth lay in the fact that only Noah and his family escaped from the destruction of the Deluge, so that the whole world had to be repopulated from this one stock, and 'the first king in every country was Noah'.[11] From this statement we can see that Blake who, as I hope to show, agreed with Milton 'that Writers of good antiquity, and ablest judgement have bin perswaded that ev'n the school of *Pythagoras* and the *Persian* wisdom took beginning from the old Philosophy of this Iland'[12] was not indulging in a mad flight of fancy when he declared that 'Adam was a Druid, and Noah also',[13] but was merely making sense from two statements which were easily correlated.

It is interesting to note, incidentally, that the problem of the Deluge has been overcome by the neo-euhemerists, the believers in the Cosmic Ice Theory of Hans Hoerbiger,[14] who postulate a terrestial cataclysm caused

several hundred thousand years ago by the disintegration
of the Tertiary satellite (the Earth's moon before its
capture of Luna some 13,500 years ago), and who therefore can fit together the jigsaw of mythological pieces,
supplied by widely separated tribes, in a way which at
least appears to be convincing and which makes some
sort of representational picture.

Bryant and his fellows, however, entangled by their
horns in the Scriptural thicket, had to struggle with the
difficulty of mankind's having, in fact, had two first-
fathers—Adam and Noah. In the creation of their chronological theories they had to prove that all mythologies
were essentially the same in their origins, deriving from
only one major and genuine source, true history as it
was related in the first books of the Bible. For instance,
a very fine example of the way in which the myth needed
to be corrected is given by Captain Francis Wilford, in
an essay *On the Chronology of the Hindus*, where he says
that 'the only material difficulty in supposing *Prîthu* to
be the same with *Noah*, respects his offspring to the fourth
generation before the flood. But, when we consider that
Noah was 500 years old when. *Japheth* and his two sons
were born, it is hardly credible that he should have had
no children till that advanced age.'[15]

In connection with Wilford it is of some importance to
note that, like Milton and Blake, he wished to prove that
the British Isles were the seat of all ancient wisdom, even
to the extent of discovering that they were the true
situation of the Garden of Eden, a supposition only
possible for a man who had been exiled in India long
enough to forget the climate. He wrote, 'In the first
passage I met with, in the *Purânas*, relating to the *sacred
isles* in the west, by which we are to understand the *British*
islands, *Iceland* and *Fero*, it is positively declared that
they are situated to the east of *Scanda-dwîp*, which is
Scandia, or *Scandinavia*; accordingly I looked for them in

the seas, to the eastwards of that famous peninsula, particularly as PLINY seems to place there the island of *Elixoia,* supposed by some, to be the abode of the blessed: but my chief pandit warned me, with much earnestness not to be too hasty: that this instance from the *Puránas* was deemed to be the only one, in which the *sacred isles* were asserted to be to the eastward of *Scandia;* and that he would produce numerous passages in which these islands were declared to be to the westward of *Scanda-dwíp,* or in a derivative form *Scandéya:* and that, from numberless particular circumstances, he would prove to my utmost satisfaction, that *Scandéya* was really to the eastward of *Samudrantaraca,* a name by which the *sacred isles* are sometimes called, because they are in the middle of the ocean. As the *Bráhmens* would rather suppose the whole economy of the universe disturbed, than question a single fact related in their sacred books, he then informed me, that this single passage alluded to a remote period, in which the poles of the globe, the course of the sun, were different from what they are now, in consequence of which there was a time, when the sun appeared to the inhabitants of *Scandia,* to rise above the *sacred isles.*' [16]

It is a pity to have to confess that after Captain Wilford had expounded his theory at very considerable length and with no small amount of detail, it emerged that his pundit, realizing his employer's obsession, had been indulging in forgery both to satisfy the gullible Captain and to stabilize the economy of his own private universe. The major work planned by Wilford was never published and, as an honest man, he acknowledged publicly that he had been imposed upon, but the theories which he had expounded had more effect upon the minds of the public than his withdrawal of some of them, so that for a good many years they were generally accepted as proof of the oneness of mythology and of the supreme position which the British Isles had formerly enjoyed.

Deriving from the Biblical story, also, was the theory of the migration of families, connected with the myth of the Tower of Babel (presumably originally one of a series of towers built with the intention of propping up Heaven to prevent a repetition of the Deluge). That Blake viewed the story of Babel in a mystical way as well as from the point of view of a speculative mythologist we know from his statement about 'Nimrod's tower, which I conjecture to have spread over many Countries; for he ought to be reckon'd of the Giant brood',[17] a statement which goes rather further than merely including Nimrod in the ranks of the traditional Titans.

Yet it was the study of this migratory activity, supposedly caused by the fall of Babel, coupled with the growing realization that the historical point of view was not only concerned with battles and crowned heads, which in due course led to the scientific study of comparative philology, a study led by Sir William Jones who recognized that 'The *Sanskrit* language, whatever be its antiquity, is of a wonderful structure; more perfect than the Greek, more copious than the Latin, and more exquisitely refined than either; yet bearing to both of them a stronger affinity, both in the roots of verbs, and in the forms of grammar, than could possibly have been produced by accident; so strong indeed that no philologer could examine them all three without believing them to have sprung from *some common source*, which perhaps no longer exists'.[18]

The historical approach was encouraged by the then rather unorthodox researches of Lord Monboddo who believed, in direct opposition to the theologians, that it 'is clearly disproved by fact and experience, as well as argument, that man, in his original state, is rational and political. I think I have shown that his natural state is no other than that of the mere animal; and therefore he can only be subject to that common law of the animal nature, well known by the name of *instinct*; a law much

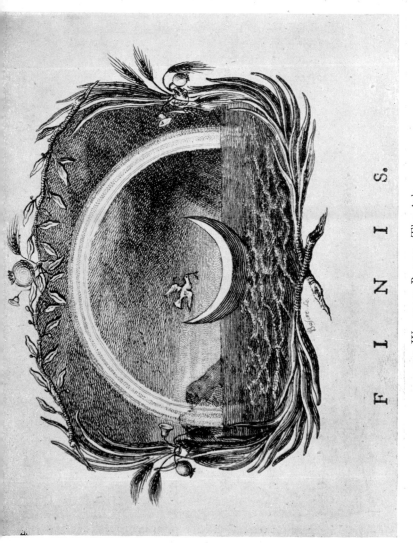

F I N I S.

12. WILLIAM BLAKE. The Ark

13. WILLIAM BLAKE. God Moving on the Face of the Waters

superior to all laws of human institution, or founded upon human institutions, and proceeding from a much higher original.'[19]

In Monboddo we can witness the breaking down of the scriptural authority, an authority which he is inclined to replace with that of Jean Jacques Rousseau, yet if it had not been for the earnest inquiries of his hog-tied predecessors, firmly restrained from wandering, he would not have been able to have erected his ingenious structure on the subject of language.

To return to the subject of William Blake's familiarity with the works of the speculative mythologists, we have his own words expressing his high opinion of Bryant's *magnum opus*, where he writes: 'The antiquities of every Nation under Heaven, is no less sacred than that of the Jews. They are the same thing, as Jacob Bryant and all antiquaries have proved.'[20]

In addition to this there is Mr. A. G. B. Russell's suggestion[21] of an even closer link with the book, namely, that while an apprentice under James Basire, from 1771 to 1778, Blake may have engraved some of the plates which bear his master's signature; 'the figure of a nude woman in the centre of sheet inscribed "Hieroglyphica Sacra"'; [22], [23] and, more particularly, that he may have designed as well as engraved 'a Vignette of the Deluge on p. 601 of vol. iii:—the dove returns to the ark (a strange crescent-shaped affair), with an olive leaf in its mouth; a vast rainbow overarches the desolate waters; a wreath of leaves and fruit surrounds the design; the treatment of the water is here especially Blake-like (cp. his rendering of the sea in the print of "Joseph of Arimathea", engraved only a very little earlier)'.[24] In addition to this engraving there are three other designs to which I would like to draw attention in connection with this little vignette. The crescent-moon Ark, as Mundane Shell, appears floating on the waters in the

D

illustration, on page 24 of *Jerusalem*, and then there is the little study of wind-tossed sea, known as *God moving on the Face of the Waters*,[25] and the water colour, dated 1805, of Noah and the Rainbow, called *The Covenant*[26] (a design which Blake was later to employ again in *Job's Sacrifice* in his series of *Illustrations of the Book of Job*). A careful study of these designs, and of the technique employed in engraving, leaves me in no doubt that, not only was Blake familiar with the book while working under Basire in Lincoln's Inn Fields, but that he certainly designed and executed this charming little vignette.

It must, however, be realized that, while Blake accepted the work of Bryant and drew largely from him and the contemporary mythologists, everything was transformed through another influence, Jacob Boehme's 'were it not that the performances, effects and works that are wrought in this mortal life, do follow the soul in the world to come, and are represented distinctly and particularly to the soul as thoughts to the mind; and as the actions of great victors are set forth in shows of triumph: it were in vain to spend our time here in anything but drowsiness and sleep.'[27]

So, where the mythologists saw a Golden Age preceding the Universal Deluge, for Blake the Golden Age was not only antediluvian but also continually existent in Eternity: 'The Nature of Visionary Fancy, or Imagination, is very little known, & the Eternal nature & permanence of its ever Existent Images is consider'd as less permanent than the things of Vegetative & Generative Nature; yet the Oak dies as well as the Lettuce, but Its Eternal Image & Individuality never dies, but renews by its seed; just so the Imaginative Image returns by the seed of Contemplative Thought; the Writings of the Prophets illustrate these conceptions of the Visionary Fancy by their various sublime & Divine Images as seen in the World of Vision. . . . Let it here be Noted that the Greek

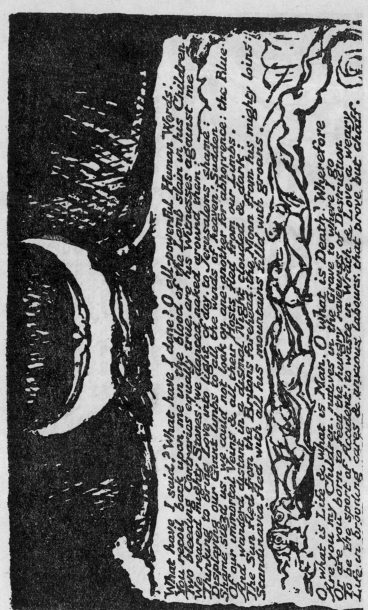

The Crescent Ark. From *Jerusalem*, p. 24

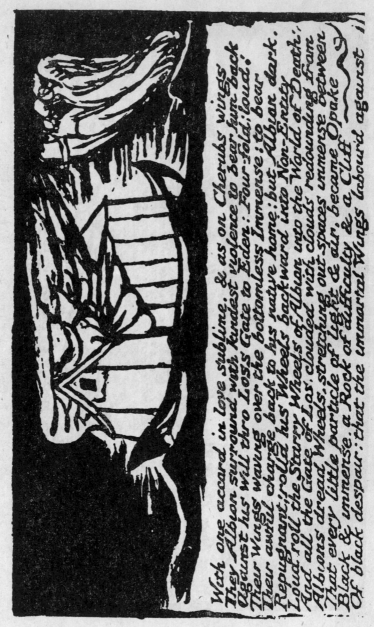

The Winged Ark. From *Jerusalem*, p. 44

Fables originated in Spiritual Mystery & Real Visions, which are lost & clouded in Fable & allegory, while the Hebrew Bible & the Greek Gospel are Genuine, Preserv'd by the Saviour's Mercy. The Nature of my Work is Visionary or Imaginative; it is an endeavour to Restore what the Ancients call'd the Golden Age. This world of Imagination is Infinite & Eternal, whereas the world of Generation, or Vegetation, is Finite & Temporal. There exist in that Eternal World the Permanent Realities of Every Thing which we see reflected in this Vegetable Glass of Nature.' [28]

Having thus applied the nitric acid of Boehme to the copperplate of Bryant, Blake's design begins to emerge from the hitherto blank and burnished surface: 'The two pictures of Nelson and Pitt are compositions of a mythological cast, similar to those Apotheoses of Persian, Hindoo and Egyptian Antiquity, which are still preserved on rude monuments, being copies from some stupendous originals now lost or perhaps buried till some happier age. The Artist having been taken in Vision into the ancient republics, monarchies, and patriarchates of Asia has seen those wonderful originals, called in the Sacred Scriptures the Cherubim, which were sculptured and painted on walls of Temples, Towers, Cities, Palaces, and erected in the highly cultivated states of Egypt, Moab, Edom, Aram, among the Rivers of Paradise, being originals from which the Greeks and Etrurians copied Hercules Farnese, Venus de Medici, Apollo Belvedere, and all the grand works of ancient art. They were executed in a very superior style to those justly admired copies, being with their accompaniments terrific and grand in the highest degree.' [29]

We can now see that the high level of culture supposed to have existed in antediluvial times and supposed to some extent to have survived in the keeping of the Patriarchs (a culture still insisted upon by the adherents of the Cosmic Ice Theory[30]), naturally consisted for Blake of the works of the painter and sculptor; for all his life Blake believed the artist to be the highest possible type of man, so that he could declare that 'A Poet, a Painter, a Musician, an Architect: the Man Or Woman who is not one of these is not a Christian',[31] which was the natural deduction to be made from his statement that 'Jesus & his Apostles & Disciples were all Artists'.[32]

Once this belief in an antediluvian and eternal art and wisdom had become fixed in Blake's mind it is clear that he had found a satisfactory explanation of his own discontent with the works of the Antique, an explanation which would have appeared eminently reasonable to those who, like Sir William Chambers, had also read the works of the mythologists: 'No man can believe that either Homer's Mythology, or Ovid's were the production of Greece or Latium; neither will any one believe, that the Greek statues, as they are called, were the invention of Greek Artists; perhaps the Torso is the only original work remaining; all the rest are evidently copies, though fine ones, from greater works of the Asiatic Patriarchs. The Greek Muses are daughters of Mnemosyne, or Memory, and not of Inspiration or Imagination, therefore not authors of such sublime conceptions. These wonderful originals seen in my visions, were some of them one hundred feet in height; some were painted as pictures, and some carved as basso relievos, and some as groupes of statues, all containing mythological and recondite meaning, where more is meant than meets the eye.'[33]

We are fortunate in being able to give an almost complete account of Blake's approach to a piece of classical sculpture, the Laocoön group.

When he was commissioned, about 1815, to draw and engrave one of the plates in illustration of John Flaxman's article on *Sculpture* in Rees's *Cyclopædia*,[34] we know that Blake visited the Royal Academy antique school,[35] to make his drawings, of which I have records of at least three.[36] However, the journeyman work of drawing and engraving was only preliminary to his own large engraving of the group, executed about 1820, in which he surrounded the figures with a mass of aphorisms and statements.[37]

The most important of these statements in connection with our present subject is the legend which Blake engraved beneath the figures, reading, ' יה [Jah, for Jehovah] & his two Sons, Satan & Adam, as they were copied from the Cherubim of Solomon's Temple by three Rhodians & applied to Natural Fact, or History of Ilium'.[38]

By 'Natural Fact' it is probable that Blake meant that their 'mythological and recondite meaning' or sacred and visionary significance had been replaced by a debased fabulous or allegorical interpretation in accordance with the careful distinction which he had made in *A Vision of the Last Judgment* when he wrote, 'The Last Judgment is not Fable or Allegory, but Vision. Fable or Allegory are a totally distinct & inferior kind of Poetry. Vision or Imagination is a Representation of what Eternally Exists, Really & Unchangeably. Fable or Allegory is Form'd by the daughters of Memory. Imagination is surrounded by the daughters of Inspiration, who in the aggregate are call'd Jerusalem. Fable is allegory, but what Critics call The Fable, is Vision itself. The Hebrew Bible & the Gospel of Jesus are not Allegory, but Eternal Vision or Imagination of All that Exists.'[39]

Blake, 'having been taken in Vision' and having seen 'the Cherubim of Solomon's Temple', could not be expected to have remained content with the copy by the 'three Rhodians' however 'justly admired' it might be. At some uncertain date, probably later than that of the execution of the didactic plate already mentioned, he started work on his own conception of the subject, imagining it as an Apotheosis, in the strict sense of the word as a 'deified ideal'. Although his drawing[40] is unfinished, there can be little doubt that it does, in fact, represent Jehovah with his two sons, Adam and Satan. An interesting point about this drawing is the existence of drapery on the figures, showing that Blake was engaged in correcting the 'three Rhodians', whose error he had already commented upon in his *Descriptive Catalogue*, in one of the notes upon his drawings, 'I understand that my Costume is incorrect, but in this I plead the authority of the ancients, who often deviated from the Habits to preserve the Manners, as in the instance of the Laocoön, who, though a priest, is represented naked'.[41]

Before going on to deal with one special aspect of Blake's indebtedness to the speculative mythologists, I will give three quotations from different periods to show how largely he was in agreement with them in their attempts to prove the unity of all 'genuine' myths. Sometime about 1778 he engraved the little collection of maxims known as *All Religions are One*, in which he laid down:

'Principle 1st. That the Poetic Genius is the true Man, and that the body or outward form of Man is derived from the Poetic Genius. Likewise that the forms of all things are derived from their Genius, which by the Ancients was call'd an Angel & Spirit & Demon . . .

'Principle 5th. The Religions of all Nations are derived from each Nation's different reception of the Poetic Genius, which is every where call'd The Spirit of Prophecy.

'Principle 6th. The Jewish & Christian Testaments are An original derivation from the Poetic Genius; this is necessary from the confined nature of bodily sensation.

'Principle 7th. As all men are alike (tho' infinitely various), So all Religions &, as all similars, have one source

'The true Man is the source, he being the Poetic Genius.'[42]

The second quotation comes from *The Marriage of Heaven and Hell*, which was probably completed about 1793. This shows Blake's realization of the way in which a myth could grow until it had become an integral part of a religion:

'The ancient Poets animated all sensible objects with Gods or Geniuses, calling them by the names and adorning them with the properties of woods, rivers, mountains, lakes, cities, nations, and whatever their enlarged & numerous senses could perceive.

'And particularly they studied the genius of each city & country, placing it under its mental deity;

'Till a system was formed, which took advantage of, & enslav'd the vulgar by attempting to realize or abstract the mental deities from their objects: this began Priesthood;

'Choosing forms of worship from poetic tales.

'And at length they pronounc'd that the Gods had order'd such things.

'Thus men forgot that All deities reside in the human breast.'[43]

Finally, in *Milton, A Poem in 2 Books*, dated between 1804 and 1808 or possibly even later, we find Blake reiterating the belief in the essential unoriginality of the Greeks and Romans:

'The Stolen and Perverted Writings of Homer & Ovid, of Plato & Cicero, which all men ought to contemn, are set up by artifice against the Sublime of the Bible; but when the New Age is at leisure to Pronounce, all will be set right, & those Grand Works of the more ancient & consciously and professedly Inspired Men will hold their proper rank, & the Daughters of Memory shall become the Daughters of Inspiration. Shakspeare & Milton were both curb'd by the general malady & infection from the silly Greek & Latin slaves of the Sword.'[44]

Of course, Blake, who was born in 1757, the year of the start of Swedenborg's new era, has looked at the euhemerist, whose point of view in a Newtonian world was often rationalist, through the eyes of a believer in revealed religion, whose mysticism could take account of the Neo-Platonists, but for whom the true and inspired man was still one of those 'who in the midst of the noise and multiplicity of church-strife, having heard the still, and secret voice of the true shepherd, are turned inwards and are attentive to the inward truth, spirit, and life of religion, searching after the spiritual instruction, which leads them to seek Christ, and his redeeming spirit, as the only safe guide from inward darkness to inward light; and from outward shadows into the substantial, ever enduring truth; which truth is nothing else, but the *everlasting union of the Soul with God, as its only good, through the spirit and nature of Christ truly formed and fully* revealed in it.'[45]

In his notes on Berkeley's *Siris*, written about 1820, Blake states his convictions, displayed in the passages quoted above, when he writes that Plato and Aristotle 'considered God as abstracted or distinct from the Imaginative World, but Jesus, as also Abraham & David, considered God as a Man in the Spiritual or Imaginative Vision. Jesus considered Imagination to be that Real Man & says I will not leave you Orphaned, I will manifest myself to you; he says also, the Spiritual Body or Angel as little Children always behold the Face of the Heavenly Father.'[46]

Although Robert Southey might tell Crabb Robinson, in 1811, that Blake had showed him 'a perfectly mad poem called *Jerusalem*—Oxford Street is in Jerusalem'[47] it is improbable that he was surprised or bewildered by the Druidic references at which I now intend to glance, for he himself had written two poems, *Madoc in Wales* and *Madoc in Aztlan*, in 1805, in which he accepted the widely prevalent idea that, along the banks of the Missouri River, there lived a Welsh-speaking tribe of American Indians—an idea so popular that at one time there was even a scheme afoot in London to raise a subscription to send a missionary to the Welsh-Indians.[48] What probably disturbed Southey was the list of unfamiliar *dramatis personæ*, performing mystically upon an eternal and not a temporal stage.

The subject of the Druids and their problematical antiquity was the hub of one of the wheels of the speculative mythologists. They believed the Druids to have had a wide influence over all peoples, basing their supposition upon the existence of a certain resemblance between the rituals employed by all primitive peoples. The Celtomanes took this to mean that all these people had learned from the Druids, or at least drew from the one deep and only original source a commonality of ritual, which is today explained on the grounds that, say, a fertility rite is bound to have certain common features no matter where it is performed as it has one end in view and all primitive races are inclined to adhere to patterns of behaviour which are, in their main outlines, similar.[49]

In the Druids were to be found the only pure inheritors of the true patriarchal religion, with which 'the christian, is but one and the same'.[50] The Rev. William Stukeley, doctor, friend of Sir Isaac Newton, and one of the earliest antiquaries to make a really strong plea for the preservation of Avebury, was firmly of the opinion that the Druids arrived in this country 'during the life of the patriarch *Abraham*, or very soon after. Therefore they brought along with them the patriarchal religion, which is so extremely like Christianity, that in effect it differ'd from it only in this; they believed in a Messiah who was to come into the world, as we believe in him that is come.

Further, they came from that very country where *Abraham* liv'd, his sons and grandsons; a family God almighty had separated from the gross of mankind, to stifle the seeds of idolatry; a mighty prince, and preacher of righteousness. And tho' the memoirs of our Druids are extremely short, yet we can very evidently discover from them, that the Druids were of *Abraham*'s religion intirely, at least in the earliest times, and worshipp'd the supreme Being in the same manner as he did, and probably according to his example, or the example of his and their common ancestors.' [51]

The great figure in the early colonization of Britain was one whom Stukeley derived from John Toland's *History of the Druids*.[52] This was the Tyrian Hercules whom he took 'to be a principal planter of *Britain*' [53] and one of Noah's great grandsons. This personage was a great builder of serpent-temples and it was he who, as an infant, was reputed to have strangled the serpents in his cradle.

Stukeley was deeply interested in the subject of the symbol of the serpent which has always been widely employed 'to signify the general attribute of immortality',[54] and he believed Avebury to have been one of those temples designed in the shape of a serpent, a theory which has been destroyed by the work of restoration carried out by modern archaeologists. He sought through East and West for other temples built to this design, and of course Blake 'believing with Milton the ancient British History' [55] could not be expected to pass this by, but pounced on 'The Serpent Temples thro' the Earth, from the wide Plain of Salisbury'.[56] (Incidentally, when M. Denis Saurat drew attention to this line in *Jerusalem*, he stated that Stukeley connected 'Stonehenge with serpent worship',[57] a strange error, for Stukeley's serpent-temple was Avebury, and the serpent is treated by him as an object of symbolical importance, not connected in any way with the worship of the reptile.)

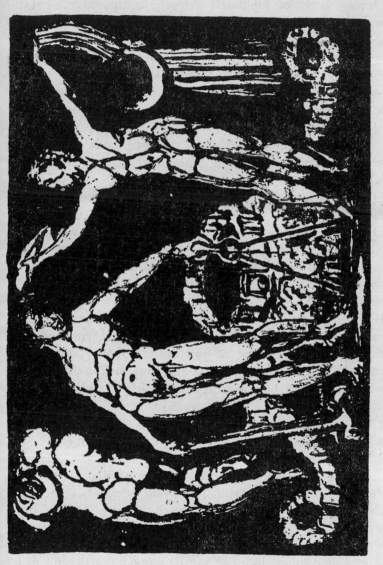

The Serpent Temple. From *Jerusalem*, p. 100

Some of Stukeley's followers, and in particular Edward Davies, were not contented with the comparatively great antiquity which he had given to the Druids. Davies wished to carry their origins even further back, to a period before the Deluge, and to do this he hunted eagerly through Mediæval Welsh Poetry, seeking for references to Noah, for, like the English mythologists, he inclined to the view that all the earliest events of history had taken place in these islands.[58]

Another of the Druidical mythologists, one who made the distinction between a legendary and an historical King Arthur to which I will refer again, was William Owen Pughe. That Blake knew Pughe we are informed by Southey, who wrote, 'My old acquaintance William Owen, now Owen Pugh, who for love of his native tongue composed a most laborious Welsh Dictionary, without the slightest remuneration for his labour, when he was in straitened circumstances, and has, since he became rich, translated *Paradise Lost* into Welsh verse, found out Blake after the death of Joanna Southcott, one of whose four-and-twenty elders he was. Poor Owen found everything which he wished to find in the Bardic system, and there he found Blake's notions, and thus Blake and his wife were persuaded that his dreams were old patriarchal truths, long forgotten, and now re-revealed. They told me this, and I, who well knew the muddy nature of Owen's head, knew what his opinion upon such a subject was worth.'[59]

It can, perhaps, be assumed that Southey was in error in dating Pughe's acquaintanceship with Blake *after* the death of Joanna Southcott, an event which occurred at the end of 1814, for long before that Blake was friendly with William Sharp, the line-engraver, who had been a disciple of Richard Brothers, 'the nephew of the Almighty' and founder of the British-Israelites, and had become one of Pughe's fellow elders as a follower of the unfortunate Devonshire prophetess. Sharp tried to convert

Druidic Arch. From *Jerusalem*, p. 70

Blake to the faith,[60] and we have Blake's rejection of the
idea in his lines *On the Virginity of the Virgin Mary &
Johanna Southcott*:

> 'Whate'er is done to her she cannot know,
> And if you ask her she will swear it so.
> Whether 'tis good or evil none's to blame:
> No one can take the pride, no one the shame.'[61]

It does not much matter whether Blake did know Pughe
personally at an earlier date than that suggested by
Southey, for I have already started to show his familiarity
with the theories of the Druidists, and there has recently
come to my notice a further possible closer link between
Blake and the theorists than even that supplied by his
writings. This is a medal, certainly dating back to the
early years of the nineteenth century, which belongs to
the Ancient Druids United Brotherhood and which is
reputed to have been designed by Blake. In this there is a
circle representing Stonehenge which closely resembles the
imaginary circles engraved by him in *Milton* and *Jerusalem*
and which is sufficiently unlike either Stonehenge or
Avebury to make the attribution seem reasonable.[62]

It now remains to show that the works of the Druidical
writers, particularly those published about the end of the
eighteenth century, were certainly known to Blake. The
subject of his lost painting of *The Ancient Britons* is
derived from the Welsh triads, which Blake was convinced
were of considerable antiquity,[63] and it seems clear that
he deviated from Stukeley, who believed the Druids to be
postdiluvial, and adhered to Edward Davies who would
have found nothing wrong with Blake's statement that
'Abraham was called to succeed the Druidical age, which
began to turn allegoric and mental signification into
corporeal command, whereby human sacrifice would have
depopulated the earth'.[64] Further, it seems highly probable
that Blake had some memory of Pughe's 'Arthur is the

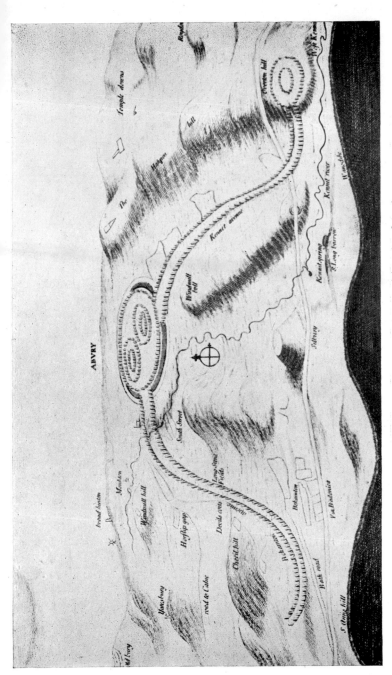

14. WILLIAM STUKELEY. The Serpent Temple of Avebury

15. WILLIAM BLAKE. The Covenant

Albion. From *Jerusalem*, p. 25

Great Bear, as the epithet literally implies: and perhaps this constellation being so near the pole, and visually describing a circle in a small space is the origin of the famous round table',[65] when he wrote 'Arthur was a name for the constellation Arcturus, or Boötes, the keeper of the North Pole'.[66]

In the creation of his vast spectral character, Albion, we now come to another writer who must have had considerable, if indirect influence on Blake. This was Jean Sylvain Bailly, whose books enjoyed a great success in England, even if he failed to take the Druids into account in his theory that the continent of Atlantis had been situated somewhere near the North Pole and that Nova Zembla, Spitzbergen, Greenland and Iceland are remnants of it.[67] Blake, engaged in enlarging mythology for his own purposes, must have been attracted by this and found that 'The giant Albion was Patriarch of the Atlantic; he is the Atlas of the Greeks, one of those the Greeks called Titans. The stories of Arthur are the acts of Albion, applied to a Prince of the fifth century.'[68] It will be noticed that Blake is now dealing with a pre-Biblical and eternal period in which the mythological Arthur, besides being a constellation, had become 'Albion, our Ancestor, patriarch of the Atlantic continent, whose History Preceded that of the Hebrews & in whose Sleep, or Chaos, Creation began; at their head the Aged Woman is Britannica, the Wife of Albion: Jerusalem is their daughter'.[69]

It should be made clear that by the end of the eighteenth century Jerusalem had become far more than a city in a far country, the wild goose once hunted by half-forgotten crusaders. It had become a symbol and as such it was bound to strike a responsive chord in the imaginations of the believers in revealed religion. How important, in fact, the symbol had become we can see from the evidence of Richard Brothers who planned to rebuild the city in

accordance with a plan divinely revealed to him.[70] And
that Jerusalem had also become personalized we know
from many sources; among them Joanna Southcott, whose
continual cry was, 'But if ye awake, O Zion, and put on
your beautiful garments, O Jerusalem, then shall your
light break forth as the morning, and your righteousness
appear as the noon-day sun'.[71] This personalization was
very much more extensive and vivid than that which
appears in the Bible itself, and it might be said that these
minor prophets used the term Jerusalem to signify the
blessed and primitive state of innocent belief, so that
those who, like Blake, were also convinced that the British
Isles were the centre of all primitive and patriarchal goodness, had little distance to travel to the point where
Jerusalem became a personification of a future, or eternal,
heaven upon earth centred in these islands. This state of
blessedness, or Jerusalem, already existed in the imaginations of those who had returned to an understanding of the
true God, with all the cruelty and wrath of the Old
Testament stripped away, and would become common
when all men accepted 'the religion of Jesus, the Everlasting Gospel'[72] which had nothing to do with the man
Jesus of Nazareth, but was the original and eternal
religion, the religion of the Druids and the Patriarchs.
It may be noted that the whole subject of the mythology
of Jerusalem in the eighteenth century requires investigation but is too large to enter into here.

I should by now have given enough examples to make
it clear that the following quotation from Blake's *Jerusalem*
would have appeared simple and, if not eminently reasonable, at least credible to his contemporaries:

'TO THE JEWS

'Jerusalem the Emanation of the Giant Albion! Can
it be? Is it a Truth that the Learned have explored?
Was Britain the Primitive Seat of the Patriarchal Religion?

If it is true, my title-page is also True, that Jerusalem was & is the Emanation of the Giant Albion. It is True and cannot be controverted. Ye are united, O ye Inhabitants of Earth, in One Religion, The Religion of Jesus, the most Ancient, the Eternal & the Everlasting Gospel. The Wicked will turn it to Wickedness, the Righteous to Righteousness. Amen! Huzza! Selah!

"All things Begin & End in Albion's Ancient Druid Rocky Shore."

'Your Ancestors derived their origin from Abraham, Heber, Shem and Noah, who were Druids, as the Druid Temples (which are the Patriarchal Pillars & Oak Groves) over the whole Earth witness to this day.

'You have a tradition, that Man anciently contain'd in his mighty limbs all things in Heaven & Earth: this you received from the Druids.

'"But now the Starry Heavens are fled from the mighty limbs of Albion."

'Albion was the Parent of the Druids, & in his Chaotic State of Sleep, Satan & Adam & the whole World was Created by the Elohim.'[73]

I hope that, in this comparatively short study, I have succeeded in showing that many of the apparent difficulties in Blake's work, which could not be explained or clarified by even the most intensive reading of the mystics, are simple once we understand that he adopted the euhemerist and Druidical attitude subscribed to by so many of his contemporaries, and that some of the difficulties have been created by our own willingness to accept any but a purely psychological interpretation of the myth. That a reading of the books I mention will not remove all the difficulties I know only too well, but I am equally sure that the realization of the part they played in the creation of Blake's universe makes it easier for us to approach and understand his essentially simple message, of the existence of the Everlasting Gospel.

16. WILLIAM BLAKE. Jehovah with his two sons Satan and Adam

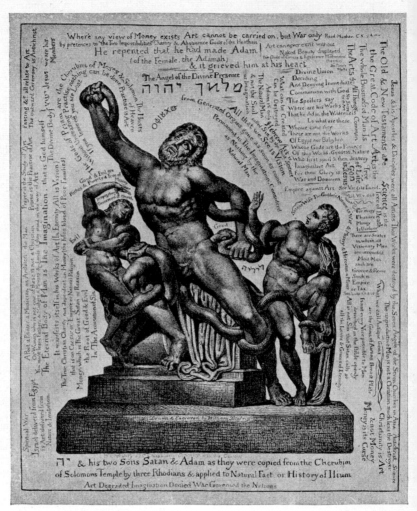

17. WILLIAM BLAKE. Laocoön

REFERENCES

1 *The Poetry and Prose of William Blake*, ed. Geoffrey Keynes, London, 1939, ed., p. 609. *A Descriptive Catalogue*, 1809.

2 *Blake and Modern Thought*, London, 1929, part II, *Celts and Druids*.

3 Julian Huxley, *Evolution The Modern Synthesis*, London, 1942, p. 17.

4 Edward Davies, *Celtic Researches on the Origin, Traditions and Language, of the Ancient Britons; with some Introductory Sketches on Primitive Society*, London, 1804, p. 5.

5 W. H. Auden and John Garrett, *The Poet's Tongue*, London, 1935, p. v.

6 *A New System; or, An Analysis of Ancient Mythology: Wherein an Attempt is Made to Divest Tradition of Fable; and to Reduce The Truth to Its Original Purity*, 3 vols., London, 1774–6; second ed., 1775–6. I quote from the second edition.

7 Bryant, *op. cit.*, i, x–xii.

8 *Ibid.*, i, xii.

9 *The Botanic Garden; A Poem*, London, 1791, i, 63 *note*.

10 *A Treatise on the Decorative Part of Civil Architecture*, The Third Edition, London, 1791. The two earlier editions do not contain the attack on the Greeks.

11 Bryant, *op. cit.*, i, xiii.

12 *Areopagitica*, 24 Nov. 1644, *Milton Complete Poetry and Selected Prose*, ed. E. H. Visiak, London, n.d., p. 716.

13 Blake, *ed. cit.*, pp. 608–9.

14 See H. S. Bellamy, *Moons, Myths and Man*, London, 1936; *The Book of Revelation is History*, London, 1942; *Built before the Flood*, London, 1943, etc.

15 *Asiatic Researches; or, Transactions of the Society instituted in Bengal, for inquiring into the History and Antiquities, The Arts, Sciences, and Literature, of Asia*, London, 1799, v, 256. [Calcutta, 1797.]

[16] *On Mount Caucasus*, in *Asiatic Researches*, London, 1800, vi, 490. [Calcutta, 1798.]

[17] Blake, *ed. cit.*, p. 867. Letter to Thomas Butts, 6 July 1803.

[18] *The Works of Sir William Jones*, ed. Lord Teignmouth, London, 1804, ii, 286.

[19] *Of the Origin and Progress of Language*, 6 vols., Edinburgh, 1773, i, 291–2.

[20] Blake, *ed. cit.*, pp. 609–10.

[21] *The Engravings of William Blake*, London, 1912, p. 191.

[22] *Ibid.*, p. 191.

[23] Bryant, *op. cit.*, ii, pl. vi.

[24] Russell, *op. cit.*, p. 191.

[25] In the collection of Esmond Morse, Esq.

[26] In the collection of Mrs. Frances White Emerson.

[27] *Mysterium Magnum Or An Exposition of the First Book of Moses called Genesis*, Translated by John Sparrow, ed. C. J. B. [Barker], London, 1924, i, xxi. [Sparrow's translation, 1654.]

[28] Blake, *ed. cit.*, pp. 638–9.

[29] *Ibid.*, p. 594.

[30] H. S. Bellamy, *Moons, Myths and Man*, p. 139, etc.

[31] Blake, *ed. cit.*, p. 582.

[32] *Ibid.*, p. 580.

[33] *Ibid.*, pp. 594–5.

[34] *The Cyclopædia; or, Universal Dictionary of Arts, Sciences and Literature*, London, 1820, plates, vol. iv, pl. vi.

[35] Alexander Gilchrist, *Life of William Blake*, ed. Ruthven Todd, London and New York, 1942, p. 261. [1863, 1880.]

[36] One of these, with a note by Frederick Tatham from which Gilchrist seems to have derived his information, is in the collection of W. Graham Robertson, Esq., and the carefully finished engraver's drawing for the plate in *The Cyclopædia* was in the collection of Lt.-Col. W. E. Moss and is now in America.

37 My reproduction is of the finer impression of two known, in the collection of Geoffrey Keynes, Esq.

38 Blake, *ed. cit.*, p. 580.

39 *Ibid.*, pp. 637–8.

40 Now in the collection of Geoffrey Keynes, Esq.; this has not been previously reproduced.

41 Blake, *ed. cit.*, p. 615.

42 *Ibid.*, pp. 148–9.

43 *Ibid.*, p. 185.

44 *Ibid.*, p. 375.

45 *An Extract from The Rev. Mr. Law's Later Works* [ed. John Wesley], Bristol, 1768, ii, 102–3.

46 Blake, *ed. cit.*, p. 818.

47 *Henry Crabb Robinson on Books and their Writers*, ed. Edith J. Morley, London, 1938, i, 41.

48 I am indebted for this information to Edward B. Hungerford, *Shores of Darkness*, New York, 1941, p. 83. I did not find this book, which also deals with the speculative mythologists and which covers some of the same ground, until I had practically finished revising this study. The earliest account of these Welsh-Indians would seem to be that of the Rev. Morgan Jones, 10, iii, 1685–6, printed by R. T. Gunther, *Early Science in Oxford*, Oxford, 1939, xii, 327–8.

49 See Ruth Benedict, *Patterns of Culture*, Boston and New York, 1934.

50 William Stukeley, *Abury, A Temple of the British Druids, with Some Others, Described*, London, 1743, p. 4.

51 William Stukeley, *Stonehenge: A Temple Restor'd to the British Druids*, London, 1740, p. 2.

52 John Toland, *A Critical History of the Celtic Religion and Learning: containing an account of the Druids*, London, n.d. [1718.]

53 Stukeley, *Abury*, p. 70.

54 R. P. Knight, *An Inquiry into the Symbolical Language of Ancient Art and Mythology*, London, 1818, p. 16.

[55] Blake, *ed. cit.*, p. 609.

[56] *Ibid.*, p. 542.

[57] Saurat, *op. cit.*, p. 53.

[58] Davies, *op. cit.*, and also his *The Mythology and Rites of the British Druids*, London, 1809.

[59] *The Correspondence of Robert Southey with Caroline Bowles*, ed. E. Dowden, Dublin, 1881, pp. 193–4.

[60] *Blake, Coleridge, Wordsworth, Lamb, etc., being Selections from the Remains of Henry Crabb Robinson*, ed. Edith J. Morley, Manchester, 1922, p. 1.

[61] Blake, *ed. cit.*, p. 107.

[62] I am indebted to Mr. Geoffrey Keynes for drawing my attention to this medallion.

[63] See, for instance, Sharon Turner, *A Vindication of the Genuineness of the Ancient British Poems*, London, 1803, for a discussion of the antiquity of these poems.

[64] Blake, *ed. cit.*, p. 609.

[65] William Owen [Pughe], *The Cambrian Biography; or, Historical Notices of Celebrated Men among the Ancient Britons*, London, 1803, p. 15.

[66] Blake, *ed. cit.*, p. 608.

[67] See *Lettres sur l'Atlantide de Platon et sur l'ancienne histoire de l'Asie*, London and Paris, 1779.

[68] Blake, *ed. cit.*, p. 609.

[69] *Ibid.*, p. 643.

[70] See *A Description of Jerusalem: Its Houses and Streets . . . with the Garden of Eden in the Centre*, with plans, London, 1801.

[71] *Copies of Letters sent to the Clergy of Exeter, From 1796 to 1800*, London, 1813, p. 7.

[72] Blake, *ed. cit.*, p. 610.

[73] *Ibid.*, p. 463.

THE REPUTATION AND
PREJUDICES OF HENRY FUSELI

'DESERVE, but expect not, to be praised by your contemporaries, for any excellence which they may be jealous of being allowed to possess themselves; leave the dispensation of justice to posterity.'[1] In these words Henry Fuseli summed up his disgust and his hopes, the subject of this study.

Cézanne, unaware of the various forces which conflict to make an artist out of a man facing a stretched canvas with a loaded brush in his hand, wrote peevishly to his friend Joachim Gasquet, 'I thought that one could do good painting without attracting attention to one's private life. An artist, to be sure, wishes to raise his standard intellectually as much as possible, but the man himself must remain in obscurity.'[2]

What a man does and how he does it, depends upon what that man is and how he lives; if he has enough money to buy himself a meal when he is hungry or to get drunk when he is depressed, if he quarrels with his wife or mistress, if he cannot stand the squalling of children; if he fights against the Zeitgeist (either as a progressive or as a reactionary—it does not seem to matter which way he reacts), or is merely content to let it envelop him and bear him easily along with it, the captive of a runaway barrage-balloon: a man's work depends upon so many things, so many apparently trifling things, that it is difficult to think of anything in his life that does not concern it in some way, immediately or indirectly.

This is, or should be, the excuse of the art-historian; picking up a fragment of gossip here and a fact or a date there, a statement on one subject and the suggestion of an attitude towards another, an opinion from this man and

the reason of the enmity of that other; reading old books
of memoirs, newspaper filcs and tattered bundles of faded
letters; trying to correct the bias towards respectability
of the official biography, to see behind the smoke-screen
of success, and to fill in the encyclopædia or dictionary
outline; to present a picture of the man and consequently
of his works, both in relation to his own times, and, it
is here so many of our historians fail, in relation to the
time of writing.

Too often today the judgement of, say, a Sir Walter
Armstrong or an Algernon Graves is served up on the best
china with the best sauces, but with a complete disregard
for the fact that maggots will destroy even the primest joint
if it has been kept too long. The study of the growth and
decline of a man's reputation is often instructive.

The time of Henry Fuseli was the time of William Blake
with Jerusalem pillared on Primrose Hill, of the Gothic
Novel and Strawberry Hill ('We are more impressed by
Gothic than by Greek mythology, because the bands are
not yet rent which tie us to its magic'[3]), of Monk Lewis
flavouring terror with indecency as Sade used horror as
a wrapper for obscenity, of Joanna Southcott and the
hysterical religious pregnancy and of Richard Brothers
who met the devil, gaily clad in clothes of white and scarlet,
strolling down the Tottenham Court Road.

During this period the fabulously wealthy William
Beckford, to spite a world which had ostracized him for
a rumour of homosexuality, erected the fantastic and
tottering fabric of Fonthill Abbey to enjoy a world of his
own creation; from the lofty tower to the twelve-foot wall
around his domain he was, in truth, God, throwing open a
vista here or placing a full-grown grove there, as the passing
whim took him. It was the period during which the last
remnants of a belated and uneasy Augustan classicism
were fast fading before the full-flavoured excitements of
romanticism.

For a long time before the Bastille fell and with it a world which had been balanced on a wire, the air had been heavy and taut with the golden glare of a September day waiting for the thunder, and, once the crash had echoed round the world, the ripples of revolution continued to wash gently along the English cliffs. Even the Royal Academy did not feel quite secure, but had its members smelling out democrats as assiduously as a true member of the Labour Party smells out Communists. For instance, John Flaxman was shocked when he told Joseph Farington, on 2 March 1807, that 'He regretted that Fuseli was not continued Professor of Painting & the more so from having heard Opie's 2nd Lecture on Monday last, which He sd. had a Democratic spirit in it, & was charged with complaint of want of patronage, instancing Hogarth & Barry as great geniuses neglected'.[4]

This was also the period of the early steam engines and of amateur scientific inquiry, of the Nasmyth family dividing its time between the palette, the steel bridge and the steam-hammer, of Wilson Lowry's invention of the ruling-machine for engraving, of the Mechanics' Institutes and the penny number, still under the sway of James Lackington and about to become the kingdom of Charles Knight, ready to change The Mysteries of Udolpho and Melmoth the Wanderer for the novels of Jules Verne and the forerunners of the detective story—the Newgate novels of the 1830s and Harrison Ainsworth's Rookwood, 1834.

Mary Wollstonecraft Shelley could no longer drag her monster screaming from a blood-fed mandrake at the foot of a gallows where stale and whitened bones clacked in the autumn gales. It was no longer possible to create trolls by magic (behind the waterfall was the geologist Dean William Buckland with his hammer and collecting-case and in front were the Rev. William Gilpin and Sir Uvedale Price, noting their seismic sensations). So, Frankenstein was presented, not as an alchemist, a

Doctor Faustus bartering with the devil, but as a scientist. The scientist had become the magician, the workings of whose mind could no longer be understood by the simple and ingenuous. Earlier the inquiring gentleman could repeat the experiments of Robert Boyle and could even make some contributions to the general knowledge of electricity, but, as the experiments became more intensified and more specialized, the apparatus became too involved, expensive and difficult of management to find a place in the corner of the polite drawing room, any more than the philosophical implications could be fitted into an unoccupied corner of the mind. The scientist became the final court of appeal, so that several qualified doctors guaranteed the genuineness of Joanna Southcott's pregnancy, while William Sharp, the celebrated engraver, and William Owen Pughe, the eminent Welsh scholar, prepared the layette for the coming of the Shiloh.

It was an age of explanation and justification, when Progress had not yet become the abstract ideal that was to organize the Great Exhibition of 1851 and erect the Crystal Palace as its own memorial. Even the arts received their handsome share of analysis. Hogarth's theory that beauty was the direct consequence of a specially curved line,[5] an eccentric theory which drew few adherents, was supplanted by the decision of Burke[6] who, deriving inspiration from John Locke, declared that the beautiful was that which produced a peculiar relaxation and languor in the spectator, a seedling which, when nursed by Alison[7] and Payne Knight,[8] produced the fine flowers of the theory of association.

Once an emotion had been admitted as valid in aiding the understanding of the arts, it had to be dissected and excused. So Sir Uvedale Price, a fervent follower of Burke, impressed by the necessity of explanation, wrote: 'I am persuaded that it would be difficult to conceive any set of objects, to which, however grand in themselves, an

18. Henry Fuseli. Grave Scene

19. Henry Fuseli. Macbeth and the Armed Head

addition of terror would not give a higher degree of sublimity; and surely that must be a cause, and a principal cause, the increase of which increases the effect—the absence of which weakens or destroys it. The sea is at all times a grand object; need I say how much that grandeur is increased by the violence of another element, and again, by thunder and lightning? Why are rocks and precipices more sublime, when the tide dashes at the foot of them, forbidding all access, or cutting off all retreat, than when we can with ease approach, or retire from them? . . . The nearer any grand or terrible objects in nature press upon the mind (providing that mind is able to contemplate them with awe, but without abject fear) the more sublime will be their effects. The most savage rocks, precipices, and cataracts, as they keep their stations, are only awful; but should an earthquake shake their foundations, and open a new gulf beneath the cataract—he who, removed from immediate danger, could dare at such a moment to gaze on such a spectacle, would surely have sensations of a much higher kind, than those which were impressed upon him when all was still and unmoved.'[9]

This seems to conjure up and approve the paintings of John Martin, where vast temples and mountains topple and slide through wide cracks in the surface of the earth, and the sky is split open with the promise of a new Revelation, draining blood from the great wound of heaven into the dwarfed landscape beneath. Martin, it should be noted, dealt with a universe explicable in Biblical and miraculous terms, a universe acceptable where a mythological and magical one would not have been.

Fuseli, as was his habit, is much more concise on the subject of terror, for 'Lawrence remarked that Fuseli's letters were written in an *Epigrammatic style*, in which much sense and knowledge was condensed in a small compass, That His manner of writing was not agreeable to those authors & readers of the present day, who are captivated by a stile woven out & very different from his. Were *His matter* expressed in the manner which suits their taste, they would be enchanted by it.'[10] In his *Aphorisms on Art*, designed but never published as a companion to the *Aphorisms on Man*[11] of his friend John Caspar Lavater, which he translated from the original German in 1788, we find the following statements:

'The loathsome is abominable, and no engine of expression.

'Sympathy and disgust are the lines that separate terror from horror; though we shudder at, we scarcely pity what we abominate.

'The axe, the wheel, sawdust, and the blood-stained sheet are not legitimate substitutes of terror.'[12]

Both Price and Fuseli have the same object, the explanation of the attraction of the terrible and the justification of that attraction. Both seek to define the terrible, but while Price would have refused to admit the magical as a cause of terror in his mind, for he was of the family of Blake's Urizen, a product of the age of reason living in a work formulated by Locke and Newton, Fuseli drew from the imagination which knows no bounds of logic and could have echoed Blake's proud declaration, 'I question not my Corporeal or Vegetative Eye any more than I would Question a Window concerning a Sight. I look thro' it & not with it.'[13]

Shy as an archangel about his age, Fuseli snarled at some too-persistent questioner who had asked him when he was born, 'How should I know? I was born in February or March—it was some cursed cold month, as you may guess from my diminutive stature and crabbed disposition.'[14] The actual date when he was born in Zürich was 6 February 1741, but it is reported that he once took up 'a little German memoir of himself, [and] changed the date from 1741 to 1745, without adding either day or month'.[15] The son of a painter, a member of a clan of Füsslis who were painters and miniaturists,[16] of whom he mentioned only two when he came to edit a dictionary of painters[17]—his own father and his ancestor Mattias Füssli (1598–1665)— Fuseli was intended to be spared the horrors of the brush and palette and was brought up with the idea that he would become a pastor of the Lutheran Church.

His childhood seems to have been one of repression, even though 'at Eight years of age He was so passionately fond of drawing that it being the custom to send him to bed early He used to steal bits of Candles, and when the family had retired He contrived to get a light and sit up all night drawing', for 'His Father, as was the usage at Zürich, determined what His Children should be without consulting their inclinations. He resolved that Fuseli should be a Scholar, and that his brother should be a Painter, whereas it should have been reversed'; further, Fuseli himself said that 'He passed those early days in crying & drawing: every day floods of tears at being forced to read, which were relieved by stolen hours for his favourite amusement'.[18]

However, the boy's protests produced no result in the stern father and Fuseli actually was ordained. Something of the biting wit he was to show in later life appears in his choice of text for his probationary sermon, which had been the subject of much local gossip. The text he chose ran, 'What will this babbler say?'[19]

The way in which Fuseli escaped from the church is worth mentioning. He and his friend Lavater became interested in the obvious corruption of a local magistrate and, collecting all the available facts about their enemy, they produced a pamphlet[20] which resulted in his dismissal. However, the friends and relations of the disgraced man were people of some power and their determination to avenge him made Fuseli and Lavater think it more discreet to leave Zürich.

They travelled about for some time and eventually came to Berlin where Fuseli executed several illustrations for his friend J. J. Bodmer's poem *Noachide*, published in 1765, and later he moved on to Barth, where he continued his classical studies and also his tireless industry in drawing for a period of six months. Meeting Sir Andrew Mitchell, British minister to the Prussian court, Fuseli accompanied him to England, either at the end of 1763 or the beginning of 1764, taking with him a framed and glazed motto written for him by Lavater which read, 'Do but the seventh part of what thou canst.'[21]

In England, the young Swiss, who had discovered his aptitude for languages (at the end of his life he knew Greek, Latin, Hebrew, French, Italian, German and English and had acquired sufficient knowledge of Dutch to read J. C. Sepp's *Beschouwing der Wonderen Gods Minstgeachtste Schepselen of Nederlandesche Insecten*[22]), worked as a translator for the booksellers Andrew Millar and Joseph Johnson, for the former of whom he prepared an edition of the Abbé Winckelmann's *Reflections on the Painting and Sculpture of the Greeks*, a work that impressed him deeply and which, it seems likely, he introduced to his friend Thomas Banks, the sculptor, at a later date, thus helping to popularize Winckelmann's ideas in England.[23] In his lighter moments Fuseli seems to have amused himself with flirtations with Angelica Kauffmann and Mary Moser.

He was then employed as travelling tutor to the eldest son of the Earl of Waldegrave, a position which he vacated after slapping his insolent pupil and to which he would refer in after life with the remark that 'The noble family of Waldegrave took me for a bear-leader, but they found me the bear'.[24]

On returning to England, Fuseli received encouragement from Joshua Reynolds and proceeded to devote most of his energies to drawing and painting, although

20. HENRY FUSELI. The Debutante

21. HENRY FUSELI. A Midsummer Night's Dream

22. HENRY FUSELI. A Midsummer Night's Dream (Detail)

23. HENRY FUSELI. The Witch

24. HENRY FUSELI. Obscene Drawings (Details)

25. HENRY FUSELI. Obscene Drawings (Details)

26. HENRY FUSELI. The Fire Place

27b. Henry Fuseli. Standing Woman

27a. Henry Fuseli. Drawing

he found time to enter into the Rousseau controversy, then at its height, with a slim anonymous volume.[25]

For the young artist, however, there was only one place to visit. At the far end of the rainbow he could discover the Roman candle spluttering and sparkling, and to it he flew like a moth. So Fuseli went to Italy, accompanied by Dr. John Armstrong, the medical versifier of *The Art of preserving Health*, 1744, with whom he quarrelled after spending twenty-eight days on board ship. In Italy Fuseli developed such a complete and overwhelming reverence for Michelangelo that he was to be haunted by the shadow of the great Italian for the rest of his life, though in many of his own drawings the influence seems to have been transmitted by way of the engravings of the mannerists, of which he owned a fairly large collection.[26] (It is interesting to speculate about Blake's equal admiration for Michelangelo in connection with his friendship with Fuseli; it seems to me reasonable to suppose that Blake was familiar with Michelangelo's work not only from engravings but also from copies made by his friends, such as Fuseli and Flaxman.)

Back in England once more, Fuseli attracted some attention among painters and writers, although Horace Walpole noted about *The Mandrake*, exhibited in 1785, 'shockingly mad, madder than ever, quite mad'.[27] He became an associate of the Royal Academy in 1788 and a full Academician in 1790.

A legend quickly grew around the figure of Fuseli, helped by his personality which was described by James Northcote as that of 'a butterfly—ingenious and fanciful and amusing—but has no strength of mind,—timid,—capricious,—vain and affected'.[28] The same bitter-tongued painter also said, 'Fuseli, whom I know so well, has a manner with him that never appears to me like that of a gentleman, but more like that of a Swiss valet'.[29] Fuseli's own tongue was sharp enough and he could

F

exclaim about Northcote's dog, with reference to its
master's meanness, 'What, Northcote keep a dog! What
must he feed upon? Why, he must eat his own fleas',[30]
but he never reached the same standards of virulence.

There is no reason for doubting that Fuseli was
everything he was described as being by Northcote, but,
in spite of his apparent timidity, he remained one of the
few Royal Academicians who was bold enough to support
his private opinions with his public utterances. At the
annual re-election of the President of the Academy in
1794, it was discovered that, while Benjamin West had
received the overwhelming majority of the votes, one
had actually been cast for Mrs. Lloyd (*née* Mary Moser),
the flower painter; taxed with responsibility for this vote,
Fuseli, forgetting the charmer of his youth, justified it
by remarking that, so far as he could see, one old woman
was as good as another. Further, when Harlow tried to
become an Associate, the Academicians, who by that
time had become expert at excluding the misfit, thought
of his coxcombery and rejected him, against the wishes
of Fuseli, who quite honestly explained that his vote was
for the painter and not for the man, a point of view
which is so far removed from that of an R.A. that it is
hardly surprising that it was considered worth recording.[31]

The shocked Farington relates that Fuseli, a renegade
priest, 'was not an advocate for public or perhaps for
any worship, saying *everything had been given to us & we
had nothing to ask for.*—Such were the light and incon-
siderate sentiments which He uttered.'[32]

That the accusations of vanity which were thrown
against Fuseli were not without a good foundation we
know from several sources, including Mary Wollstonecraft with whom he had a peculiar and sexless intrigue
until his wife objected and he in turn discovered her to
be a 'philosophical sloven';[33] she is said at one time to
have exclaimed to him, 'I hate to see that reptile Vanity

sliming over the noble qualities of your heart'.[34] And the embittered and ungenerous Edward Dayes wrote an amusing and unsympathetic notice of Fuseli in which he says, 'A great deal might be overlooked, but for his excessive vanity which will not allow merit in others. He asserts that no man in England understands drawing but himself; and that Michael Angelo was a greater man than God Almighty: alluding to the style of figures of that artist, which he is weak enough to think surpasses Nature.'[35]

The extent to which the legend of Fuseli as monster had grown by 1805 is shown in Benjamin Robert Haydon's account of his first visit to him. He wrote, 'Galvanized devils—malicious witches brewing their incantations— Satan bridging Chaos, and springing upwards like a pyramid of fire—Lady Macbeth—Paolo and Francesca— Falstaff and Mrs. Quickly—humour, pathos, terror, blood, and murder, met one at every look! I expected the floor to give way—I fancied Fuseli himself to be a giant. I heard his footsteps and saw a little bony hand slide round the edge of the door, followed by a little white-headed lion-faced man in an old flannel dressing-gown tied round his waist with a piece of rope and upon his head the bottom of Mrs. Fuseli's work basket.'[36]

The tale of the relationship between Haydon and Fuseli, related in the autobiography of the former, is a comedy of real and imagined slights and injuries. For instance, Fuseli credited Haydon with the authorship of the violent attacks on him in *The Examiner*, written by Robert Hunt under the rather ambiguous initials, R. H. (it seems probable that Haydon had at least supplied some of the information for these though he was guiltless of the actual writing). It was one of these attacks which impelled William Blake to write, 'Such an artist as Fuseli is invulnerable, he needs not my defence; but I should be ashamed not to set my hand and shoulder, and whole

strength, against those wretches who, under the pretence
of criticism, use the dagger and the poison.'[37] How highly
Blake thought of Fuseli we know, not only from this but
also from the celebrated little epigram in which he
declared:

> 'The only Man that e'er I knew
> Who did not make me almost spew
> Was Fuseli: he was both Turk & Jew—
> And so, dear Christian Friends, how do ye do?'[38]

And that Fuseli returned the admiration is obvious not
only in the often quoted remark about Blake's being
damned good to steal from, but also in the preface he
wrote for Blake's edition of Blair's *The Grave*, where he
finishes with the remark that 'Every class of artists, in
every stage of their progress or attainments, from the
student to the finished master, and from the contriver
of ornaments, to the painter of history, will find here
materials of art and hints of improvement!'[39]

Apart from his work as an artist and as a writer of art,
Fuseli, on account of his upbringing, was generally held in
great esteem as a classical scholar by his contemporaries,
most of whom had not had a classical education; John Opie,
for instance, had the 'conviction that the learning of Mr.
Fuseli was an honour to his profession, and tended to exalt
it in the opinion of society'.[40]

Coming from a family almost as enamoured of entomology as of painting, Fuseli was a fervent student of
the subject, generally reading a book on moths or studying
drawings of insects while he ate his breakfast. There are
at least twenty-three different works on entomology in
his sale catalogue, including Moses Harris's beautiful
*Aurelian, or Natural History of English Insects, namely,
Moths and Butterflies*, 1778, as well as a collection of no
less than 203 drawings, mostly of North American insects,
by a Georgian artist, J. Abbot.[41]

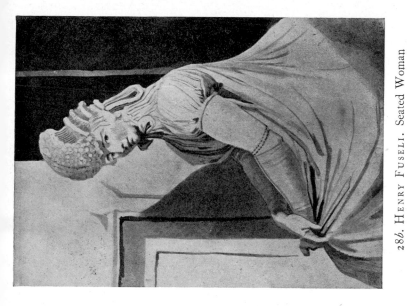

28b. HENRY FUSELI. Seated Woman

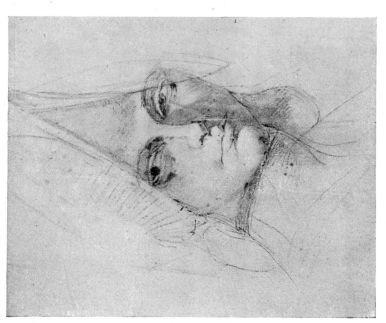

28a. HENRY FUSELI. Head

29. HENRY FUSELI. Kathleen, from *The Task*

John Knowles's dull but informative biography shows how genuine Fuseli's entomological interests were, and that he carried his enthusiasm to the point of rearing moths in his house is mentioned several times, including the letter where he proudly proclaims 'that of some pupæ of *Sphinx euphorbiæ*, found on the spurge of the Devonshire sands, I have reared, perhaps for the first time in England, two beautiful moths'.[42] The moths that he knew so well make their appearance in many of his paintings, especially in one, which is now lost, in illustration of *Lycidas*, 'where the shepherd and shepherdess (exercising the licence of the painter, he has introduced the latter) are only ten inches in length, happening to find in Mr. Johnson's garden at Fulham, a beautiful moth, he was so delighted with the insect, that in spite of all propriety and his better knowledge, he painted it the size of nature, hovering above the figures, with expanded wings'.[43]

Many of the contemporary onslaughts upon Fuseli accuse him of distorting the human body into impossible attitudes, but this line of attack seems to have been partly founded on some ignorance of the strange variety of shapes into which the human figure can be twisted. In 1824, John Henry Lavater, in a dedication addressed to Fuseli, refers to 'the energetic figures and the ingenious combinations which I beheld your creative hand draw forth frequently from the delusive obscurity of Nature, the real forms of which the eye of genius alone is capable of discerning . . . you, who are so profoundly conversant in anatomy.'[44] Perhaps a part of this eulogy can be discounted on the grounds of family friendship, as 'he was always averse to dissecting, believing the current story, that his idol, Michael Angelo, had nearly lost his life from a fever got by an anatomical examination of a human body in a state of putrefaction',[45] but Charles Bell, the surgeon, had little sentimental reason for being gentle with Fuseli's reputation (beyond the fact that the

latter voted for his appointment as Professor of Anatomy
to the Royal Academy in 1808, though without success),
and it seems certain that Bell would have pounced on
any gross anatomical inaccuracy if it had existed. In a
rather petulant letter to his brother, dated 26 July 1808,
in which he dismisses Flaxman as 'a kind of lapidary', he
writes that Fuseli is 'unquestionably a man of genius; his
sketches are remarkably fine, but often he paints a log for
a man; is rarely simple, which is an ingredient in the truly
sublime or grand. In his painting he is extravagant; in his
writing turgid and inflated, labouring and big with something he cannot express, and in his criticism more extravagant still.' [46] (It is worth remembering that both Blake and
Samuel Palmer stressed the value of 'excess', and that both
were ardent admirers of Fuseli.)

Opposed to Bell's view of Fuseli as an egg-bound
genius is the opinion of Sir Thomas Lawrence, certainly
a much greater connoisseur than artist, who showed his
appreciation of Fuseli by owning twenty-one paintings
by him. Writing to Thomas Uwins in 1825, soon after
Fuseli's death, he makes some remarks on Michelangelo
and goes on, 'We have just sustained the loss of kindred
genius, if not greater, in the original and lofty conceptions
of Mr. Fuseli. In poetic invention it is not too much to say
he has had no equal since the fifteenth or sixteenth centuries,
and if his drawings and proportions were mannered and
sometimes carried to excess, still it was exaggeration of the
grandeur of antique form, and not—as in many—enlarge-
ment of the mean and ordinary in nature.' [47]

Five years after the death of Fuseli, Haydon, seeing
in the theatrical extravagance of his former master something of his mental portrait of himself down the wrong
end of a telescope, attempted to sum up his achievement
in the following account, which, although flavoured with
his own ambitions, is obviously honest, and, within the
limits of his time, just:

'Fuzeli was undoubtedly the greatest genius of that day. His Milton gallery showed a range of imagination equal to the poet's; his Satan bridging Chaos, his Uriel watching Satan, his Shepherd's Dream, his Fairies from Shakespeare, and his Ghost in Hamlet, announce him as . . . being the greatest inventor in art since Julio Romano. But in the modes of conveying his thoughts by form, colour, light, and shadow, and above all, nature, he was a monster in design; his women are all strumpets, and his men all banditti, with the action of galvanized frogs, the dress of mountebanks, and the hue of pestilential putridity. No man had the power like Fuzeli of rousing the dormant spirit of youth; and there issued from his inspiration the nucleus of painters, who have been the firmest supporters of the British school.

'But Fuzeli, as a painter, must be a warning to all. Had he taken the trouble to convey his thoughts like the great masters, his pictures would have risen as time advanced; yet as time advances, his pictures, from having no hold on our feelings like the simplicity of nature, must sink. His conceptions, however poetical, are not enough to satisfy the mind in an art, the elements of which are laid in lovely nature; and great as his genius was in fancy and conception, inventor as he was in art of fairies and ghosts, he will never be an object to imitate, but always to avoid by young men, who are more likely to lay hold of his defects than his beauties. The finest conception of a ghost that ever was painted, was the Ghost in Hamlet on the battlements. There it quivered with martial stride, pointing to a place of meeting with Hamlet; and round its vizored head was a halo of light that looked sulphureous, and made one feel as if one actually smelt hell, burning, cindery, and suffocating. The dim moon glittered behind; the sea roared in the distance, as if agitated by the presence of a supernatural spirit; and the ghost looked at Hamlet, with eyes that glared like the light in the eyes of a lion, which is savagely growling over his bloody food. But still it was a German ghost, and not the ghost of Shakespeare. There was nothing in it to touch human sympathies combined with the infernal; there was nothing at all of "his sable, sivered beard", or his countenance more "in sorrow than in anger"; it was a fierce, demonical, armed fiend reeking from hell, who had not yet expiated "the crimes done in his days of nature", to qualify him for heaven. His next finest works were the two fairy pictures in the Shakespeare gallery, some diving into harebells, some sailing in Bottom's shoe; but beautiful as they were, indeed the only fairies ever painted, still your heart longed for nature in colour, form, action, and expression. Such an union had the Greeks, and no art in the world will be perfect until it appears again. These pictures are evidences of the highest conception of the fanciful and supernatural. His Lazar House is an evidence of his power of pathos; his Uriel and Satan of the poetical; his Puck putting on a girdle, of the humorous and mischievous. But when Fuzeli attempted the domestic, as in the illustrations of Cowper, his total want of nature stares one in the face, like the eyes of his own ghosts.' [48]

Against this estimate by the half-blind Haydon, laboriously copying the sinews of a foot from the Elgin marbles in a damp, dark shed, dreaming of a 'History picture' as large as the wall of a house, and using the stick of Winckelmann to beat the translator, we can set that of the neat Charles Robert Leslie, R.A., another pupil and the manufacturer of genteel illustrations of the classics, Stothard with the last trace of guts removed, who was, however, an honest and seldom wrong-headed critic, one who admired the early pre-Raphaelite paintings and who was not afraid to tell the painters of his admiration.

Writing twenty-five years after Haydon, he says: 'With no artist of powers as great as those of Fuseli were those powers confined within so narrow a circle; but within

The Three Witches. From *Heinrich Füssli's sämtliche Werke*, Zürich, 1807

that circle he has expressed the terror and the evanescence of the world of phantoms, with a power unequalled by any painter that ever lived. Perhaps the finest of all his works is the "Sin and Death"; and in this he has done that which, had he not done it, we might have thought impossible—he has embodied Milton's words: "What seemed his head the likeness of a kingly crown had on".

'In the "Satan" of Sir Thomas Lawrence (the worst portrait he ever painted), all is so material as to be wholly unnatural with reference to the subject. The body and limbs of the fiend are as solid as the shaft of the spear he holds; and the helmet, sword and shield seem borrowed from the property-room of a theatre. In the "Sin and Death" of Fuseli there are a ponderous key (the key of the gates of Hell) and a chain. But they are forged by no earthly smith, and are not otherwise thought of the spectator than as parts of a terrible vision.

'If what I have said of his Art be thought to contradict my urging the necessity of the study of nature to the imaginative painter, I would remark that he was profoundly acquainted with all in Nature that could help his conceptions of the visionary. He was a perfect master of chiaroscuro and of the evanescence of colour, and he possessed such a competent knowledge of the anatomical structure of the human figure as to be able to give ideal probability to attitudes in which it was impossible that he could be helped by living models. Hence, he could also give to his ghosts that general and uncertain look that belongs to shadowy beings, without the omission of the leading characteristics of form; and his breadth, to borrow an expression of his own, is never "emptiness". . . . Everybody can laugh at the extravagances that so often disfigure the works of Fuseli. But it would require eloquence equal to his own to do justice to his finest things, and in spite of his great faults, I cannot but look on him as a great genius, a genius for whom the age in which he lived was unworthy.'[49]

Reading these estimates of his stature, making allowance for the bias of contemporaries and pupils (it is noteworthy that none of his pupils, even the disappointed Haydon, ever turned completely against him), it would be reasonable to expect that Fuseli's reputation would have retained or even gained something on its high level as the nineteenth century progressed, in spite of the man who assured Blake that 'the truth is, he is a hundred years beyond the present generation',[50] for it should be remembered that many of the people who admired his work were painters, who could see, for instance, the emptiness of so much of West's work and who did not contribute to the inflation of that reputation.

Among the most interesting of Fuseli's pupils were Theodore Mattias von Holst and Thomas Griffiths Wainewright. Of the former little is known beyond the fact that he was born in 1810 and 'In his tenth year he attracted the notice of Sir Thomas Lawrence by the beauty of his pencil sketches, and subsequently executed many drawings for Sir Thomas, several of which were said to have been commissioned by the King (George IV)'.[51] William Bell Scott, who gives the best personal account of this strange painter known to me, wrote, 'Theodore von Holst, whose art was a cross between Retsch and Fuseli, which latter very able inventor anticipated great things of von Holst. There was also an element of simplicity in his composition not to be found in either of the elders. . . . von Holst fell in love, to use an old-fashioned phrase for a perrenial disease, with a wild creature, who led him into ruinous course. Shortly after my own marriage my wife and I went to a sort of public entertainment, on the opening of the Lowther Arcade, and there we were joined by von Holst, who introduced a handsome, loudly-dressed young woman as his wife. I did not like her, yet she was a noble creature, who wanted not the power of fascination nor the ability to use it. To this lady he accorded what she did not desire—the same freedom of intercourse with the opposite sex that men arrogate to themselves, but she returned him an unconquerable jealousy, and it was said at last kept a stiletto secreted in the sacred hollow of her bodice for his benefit. A sudden illness, however, in 1844, when he was thirty-three, . . . saved her from the chance of using it.

'His pictures were exactly the kind of pictures for which our school has never even allowed a place, and for which there is no London public at all. They had originality and poetry, but of a purely romantic character, without sentiment: tragic without anything theatrical or transpontine. Besides "Jairus's Daughter" I only remember two: "Mephisto drawing the Wine from the Table", and the "Genius Loci", a pale spirit in a fair landscape. But his sketches were the most astounding—the designs he would have liked to have carried out! One of them was "Satan and the Virgin Mary dancing on the Edge of the World"!'[52]

I have reproduced here an etching by von Holst after Fuseli, in my own possession, which seems to be an exaggeration of a detail in the latter's painting of *Titania and Bottom* (Tate Gallery).

Wainewright, whose fame as a forger and poisoner has overshadowed him as a painter and writer, was one of Fuseli's most steadfast admirers, and wrote of his idol 'he may be ill-apprehended, but never despised; you may hate, but cannot forget; this is the prerogative of only true and very high genius'.[53]

However, Fuseli himself was not sanguine, having 'little hope of *Poetical* painting finding encouragement in England. The People are not prepared for it. Portrait with them is everything.—Their taste & feelings all go to realities.—The idea does not operate on their minds.— *Historical* painting, viz.: Matter of fact they may encourage.'[54] Replacing the word 'historical' with 'anecdotal', this statement of Fuseli's is a pretty fair forecast of the

30. Henry Fuseli. Drawing

course of patronage from, say, 1850, and it supplies one of the reasons for his own reputation's gannet-like plunge. By 1868, at the B. G. Windus sale, his *Lycidas*[55] fetched sixteen guineas, and his most famous painting, *The Nightmare*,[56] only brought about a pound.

Part of the trouble was that Fuseli did not make a good bed-mate for one of the 'creations' (I use the word in its millinery sense) of a Francis Grant, a W. B. Richmond or an Alma-Tadema. There is a delightful story by Samuel Palmer, related in connection with his wish that the National Gallery would acquire his 'love of ancient days "Psyche coming to the Fates". "What is that?" said a lady to her mate, as I was drinking it in at Somerset House. "O! that's IMAGINATION" said he with a most contemptuous emphasis upon the words—"Come along!" giving her a vigorous pull to the next picture.'[57]

Again, the size and unavailability of most of his pictures helped the compilers of histories of English painting, who have not bothered to seek them out, or even to look carefully at the collection of his drawings in the Print Room of the British Museum, or in the Victoria and Albert Museum; the word 'Extravagant' has been handed down from one critic to another as a kind of entailed heirloom. Too many people have been interested in Blake, as a poet and as a painter, for a writer to dare to omit him, though, as a misfit, he nearly always gets a chapter to himself, the chapter where Fuseli, Palmer, Calvert and Linnell are neatly pigeonholed with an accepted line or two written on the labels tied round their necks. There was no money invested in Fuseli's pictures, so the uncomfortable creature was banished to the attic, from which he occasionally let fall a drawing which could not be dismissed as negligible or as being 'Blakean', or one of his neatly coiffured obscenities which horrify eyes focused to appreciate the 'nice' drawing-room pornography of the Rev. Matthew William Peters, R.A., or his like.

H. Fuseli inv.t et del. —   *J. M. von Holst fecit*

Etching by von Holst after Henry Fuseli

These obscene drawings are among the finest of
Fuseli's works, and they possess an extraordinary atmo-
sphere, where the faces of the actors are quite unmoved
by the strange actions which they perform; Fuseli's hair-
fetishism appears in the elaborate headdresses of the
women, whose hair, poured and moulded into fantastic
shapes, suffers no disturbance from the static violence of
which they partake. My only regret is that I am unable,
under our present dubious legal system, to reproduce
several of them here in their entirety; all that I can do
is to give some details from six of these drawings lately
in my own possession.[58]

In spite of this slurring over of his name during the nineteenth century, the stream of appreciation of Fuseli continued as a trickle, sometimes almost underground. He is highly praised by Alexander Gilchrist in his *Life of Blake*, first published in 1863, and a short and appreciative account of him was given by the brothers, Samuel and Richard Redgrave, in their *A Century of Painters of the English School*, 1866. As might have been expected, the Rossetti brothers had a very high opinion of his abilities and imagination; the artistic interests of the Rossettis are a subject that might repay investigation— Dante Gabriel bought the Blake Note-book from Samuel Palmer's hangdog brother William, the British Museum attendant, for ten shillings, borrowed from his brother, and one of the two pictures on his walls in 1848 was 'an engraving after that great painter von Holst',[59] and no doubt he was responsible for the fact that the pre-Raphaelite Brotherhood were accustomed to gather at Campbell's Scotch Stores in Beak Street where the walls were hung with von Holst's paintings,[60] and he admired and assisted James Smetham; William Michael, whose art criticism is not contemptible, paid the only recorded visit to Richard Dadd in Bedlam where he found him working on a drawing.

In the years following 1900, however, the reaction against the anecdotal in paint became so pronounced that few of those who were interested in contemporary painting cared to see anything in the eighteenth and nineteenth centuries in England, except landscape. About 1920, however, excited by the disappearance of Fuseli's drawings and paintings to Switzerland, where Professor Paul Ganz[61] has been working on an authoritative book, people in this country again began to take an interest in the oddest man and most original artist (excluding Turner, whose oddity and originality took a different form) ever to become a member of that genteel club of certified gentlemen—the

Royal Academy. Among those who, in recent years, have drawn attention to Fuseli are Mr. Sacheverell Sitwell[62] and Mr. John Piper, who wrote, 'Fuseli reappears today quite naturally. Our transitional period reflects his own. There were as many schools of painting in his day as there are now, and they were as divergent; and Fuseli's work is probably *closer* now than it has been since his death.'[63]

Today, when we are stumbling towards an understanding of our dreams, we have found in the word 'subconscious' an admirable excuse for a liking for, say, the desolate arcades and squares of Chirico, the plasmic dancing amœba of Miró and the flexible watches, the crutch-supported buttocks and the hidden images of Salvador Dali.

Like Fuseli, we have a passion for the inexplicable. For example, there is the popularity of the terrible novels and stories of Franz Kafka. Too much of the world has been tied up in neat parcels and deposited in the left-luggage office at Piccadilly Circus tube station. The mandrake has gone with the upas tree and spontaneous generation with the philosopher's stone.

We can appreciate the illogical and weird element in the story which Fuseli related to the Locks of Norbury: 'The morning of a fox hunt a large party of gentlemen met, and as they proceeded to the chase were joined by others. One among the rest was particularly distinguished by the elegance of his figure, and the activity and grace with which he rode. Lord Lyttelton, when the chase was over, invited him to return home to dinner, and there he was the most entertaining companion they had ever met. The party continued drinking late and he sat with them and endeavoured to prolong the evening, but they dropped off one by one, some under the table, others fast asleep in their seats. At length, very unwillingly, the stranger desired to be shown his chamber. Before long the most dreadful yells were heard and traced to the

Hercules and Diomedes.

From *Heinrich Füssli's sämtliche Werke*, Zürich, 1807

stranger's room; they knocked at the door and begged to know if he were ill. An angry "No!" was all they could obtain, and upon the question being repeated he desired they would return to bed. But the yells continued with such violence that they could bear it no longer and broke open the door, when to their horror the stranger appeared *streaming with blood*, and they saw that the floor and the bed were also covered with blood. He held a whip in his hand with which he seemed to have been inflicting a horrible scourging. He said he was very sorry the house had been disturbed but assured them that it was now over and they might go to sleep again, and that next day at breakfast he would explain what appeared so extraordinary to them. Next morning they waited impatiently for the promised communication, but lo! the stranger was gone. They inquired of the grooms, who related that at break of day he came down, took his horse out of the stable and disappeared.'[64]

As I have said, the majority of Fuseli's paintings are not readily accessible, but his drawings turn up occasionally and they do not suffer much in reproduction. It is in these drawings that we will probably find his most characteristic work, for there is undoubted truth in Farington's statement that 'The observations which Fuseli made of the disadvantage He has suffered from not having had proper *early* education in the art are certainly shown in his works to be just. His powers of execution cannot keep pace with his conceptions, which are generally, if not always, of a nature that particularly require vigorous practice to express them properly.'[65]

There must be many thousands of his drawings scattered around this country and in Switzerland, some of them masquerading as the works of other artists. He could, and did, employ a multitude of styles, so that we can encounter drawings that might be Italian of the sixteenth century, or, on the other hand, that might almost be by John Flaxman—not, perhaps, very good Flaxman, lacking his invincible Puritanism and hard correctness of line; and, of course, there are the drawings which show the influence of Blake just as there are the Blakes showing the influence of Fuseli, although it must be said that in neither case are these the best works of the artists.

One of the strange figures who was either influenced by Fuseli or who had some effect upon him was an almost unknown Edinburgh painter, John Brown, whom he met at Rome in the 1760s, and who died of consumption at the age of thirty-five. There is very little known about Brown except that he accompanied Charles Townley and Sir William Young as draughtsman on their anti-quarian tour of Sicily, and that he was a friend of Lord Monboddo whom he helped with the Italian section of his *Of the Origin and Progress of Language*, 1773, and who did his best to repay the debt by editing and pub-lishing Brown's letters on Italian opera and music after his death. The problem of John Brown seems to be quite insoluble at the moment, for in the Scottish collections, which I have examined, his name is always connected with careful pencil portraits and miniatures, never with the few drawings which I have seen, bearing his signature, which show the vivid unearthly reality of a rather better Beardsley and which would certainly pass as very good Fuseli. The question of whether Brown influenced Fuseli or whether the inspiration was the other way round will need to remain unanswered until there is an opportunity to examine a larger body of his work than is available at present, with the drawings that are in the collection of Sir Robert Witt and others that belonged to Arnold Otto Meyer of Hamburg.[66] The only suggestive pointer is Fuseli's own touchiness on the subject as shown in his one recorded mention of Brown, breaking peevishly across a conversation, 'Well, Brown, Brown, we have had enough of Brown; let us now talk of Cipriani, who is in hell.'[67]

Brown was closely connected with another neglected Scottish painter, Alexander Runciman, who, it is probable, also had some influence on Fuseli. The latter wrote of him that he was 'in my opinion, the best *Painter* of *us* in Rome'.[68] Alexander Runciman, who like Fuseli had dreamed of being 'a rival to Michael Angelo',[69] left as his chief work a series of frescoes in illustration of various passages in Ossian, at Penicuik, near Edinburgh, which was destroyed by fire in 1899; his brother John, who died when he was twenty-four, is another very interesting painter, some of whose work has something in common with that of Fuseli.

Fuseli was obsessed by the terrible and the colossal and, when a young man, he wrote in a friend's album, 'I do not wish to build a cottage, but to erect a pyramid'.[70] He was of the opinion that 'Common-place figures are as inadmissible in the grand style of painting as common-place characters or sentiments in poetry',[71] but he frequently failed to notice in his own work the danger which he himself had pointed out, that 'Tameness lies on this side of expression, grimace overleaps it',[72] with the result that many of his ghosts in wood-louse armour and his bristle-chinned witches show a tendency to grimace with about as much effect on the spectator as a turnip-lantern at Hallowe'en.

A hundred and thirty years before the advent of the surrealists, presumably thinking of his own painting of *The Nightmare*, he remarked that 'one of the most unexplored regions of art are dreams'.[73]

However, it is not in his grand or terrible pictures that we shall find what is perhaps his finest and certainly his most original and characteristic work. (For lack of evidence I have assumed that the connection between Fuseli and Brown was mutual, and for the same reason I ignore Mr. Sitwell's suggestion that Wainewright, a very much younger man, may have executed certain of

32. HENRY FUSELI. The Nightmare (variant)

33. HENRY FUSELI. The Nightmare

the more obscene drawings.[74]) The most striking of his works will be found among these 'domestic' drawings which Haydon failed to appreciate; drawings in which there is nothing of the domesticity envisaged by a C. R. Leslie or an Augustus Egg.

These drawings show women engaged in ordinary tasks, dressing for a ball or embroidering a scarf, or merely standing waiting; yet, into these commonplace scenes Fuseli has managed to infuse something of the pure clarity of a dream. There is intense concentration on unimportant, or seemingly so, detail, so that all the women have immense or elaborate coiffures (again we see his preoccupation with the mechanics of hair-dressing which appears only in these and in his obscene drawings), and even the placing of a cup upon a table seems to have some terrible hidden significance.

His tall, fantastic women clad in parodies of the long clinging dresses of the period are, as Haydon suggests, procuresses and whores, haggling and tempting, rather than figures from Cowper's poems, and all their everyday and trivial actions have become charged with the significance of magical rites; the terrible and the sublime pale into insignificance beside these drawings where the domestic scene enters the realm of the dream.

REFERENCES

[1] John Knowles, *The Life and Writings of Henry Fuseli*, London, 1831, iii, 70; *Aphorism 25*.

[2] *Paul Cézanne Letters*, ed. John Rewald, London, 1941, p. 198.

[3] Knowles, *op. cit.*, iii, 120; *Aphorism 105*.

[4] *The Farington Diary*, ed. James Greig, London, 1922, etc., iv, 91. The text of this edition is unfortunately completely untrustworthy.

[5] William Hogarth, *The Analysis of Beauty*, London, 1757.

[6] Edmund Burke, *A Philosophical Enquiry into the Origin of our Ideas of the Sublime and Beautiful*, London, 1757.

[7] Archibald Alison, *Essays on the nature and principals of Taste*, Edinburgh, 1790.

[8] Richard Payne Knight, *An Analytical Inquiry into the Principles of Taste*, London, 1805.

[9] *Sir Uvedale Price on the Picturesque*, ed. Sir Thomas Dick Lauder, Edinburgh and London, 1842, pp. 102-3. [1801.]

[10] *The Farington Diary*, iv, 60.

[11] John Caspar Lavater, *Aphorisms on Man*, London, 1788.

[12] Knowles, *op. cit.*, iii, 89, 91; *Aphorisms 86, 87, 91*.

[13] *The Poetry and Prose of William Blake*, ed. Geoffrey Keynes, London, 1939 ed., p. 652.

[14] Allan Cunningham, *The Lives of the most eminent British Painters, Sculptors and Architects*, second edition, London, 1830, ii, 269. This anecdote does not appear in the first edition, published in the same year.

[15] *Ibid.*, ii, 269.

[16] See Arnold Federmann, *Johann Heinrich Füssli, Dichter und Maler*, Zürich and Leipzig, 1927, p. 168.

[17] M. Pilkington, *A Dictionary of Painters*, ed. Henry Fuseli, London, 1805; new edition 1810.

[18] *The Farington Diary*, ii, 46.

[19] Knowles, *op. cit.*, i, 18; the quotation is from *Acts*, xvii, 18.

20 *Der ungerechte Landvogt oder die Klagen eines Patrioten,* Zürich, 1762. I have not seen a copy of this.

21 'Thue den siebenden Theil von dem was du thun kannst.' Knowles, *op. cit.,* i, 29.

22 Knowles, *op. cit.,* i, 355–6. I take the title from *A Catalogue of the Small and very Select Classical Library of the late Henry Fuseli,* Sotheby, London, July 22, etc., 1825, lot 259.

23 *Annals of Thomas Banks,* ed. C. F. Bell, Cambridge, 1938, pp. 17–18.

24 Knowles, *op. cit.,* i, 42.

25 *Remarks on the writings and conduct of J. J. Rousseau,* London, 1767. This book is excessively rare, a fire at the publishers having destroyed the greater part of the stock.

26 See *Sale Catalogue, cit.,* 1825.

27 William T. Whitley, *Artists and their Friends in England, 1700–1799,* London and Boston, 1928, ii, 37

28 *Conversations of James Northcote, R.A., with James Ward on Art and Artists,* ed. Ernest Fletcher, London, 1901, p. 125.

29 John Thomas Smith, *Nollekens and his times,* London, 1828, ii, 416.

30 Knowles, *op. cit.,* i, 164.

31 Knowles, *op. cit.,* i, 318.

32 *The Farington Diary,* v, 4.

33 Knowles, *op. cit.,* i, 164.

34 *Ibid.,* i, 363.

35 *The Works of the late Edward Dayes: containing . . . Professional Sketches of Modern Artists,* ed. E. W. Brayley, London, 1805, p. 326.

36 *Life of Benjamin Robert Haydon, from his autobiography and journals,* ed. Tom Taylor, London, 1853, i, 25. Most of what Haydon says on Fuseli here and elsewhere is condensed in his *Lectures on Painting and Design* [vol. ii], London, 1846, Lecture viii, Fuzeli.

37 Blake, *ed. cit.,* p. 911.

38 *Ibid.,* p. 662.

39 *The Grave: A Poem by Robert Blair, Illustrated by Twelve Etchings*, London, 1808, p. xiv.

40 Amelia Opie, *Lectures on Painting by the late John Opie, to which are prefixed a memoir*, London, 1809, p. 28.

41 See *Sale Catalogue, cit.*, 1825.

42 Knowles, *op. cit.*, i, 298.

43 *Ibid.*, i, 362.

44 *An Introduction to the Study of the Anatomy of the Human Body*, London, 1824, pp. iii–iv.

45 Knowles, *op. cit.*, i, 48.

46 William T. Whitley, *Art in England*, 1800–1820, Cambridge, 1928, p. 127.

47 William T. Whitley, *Art in England*, 1821–1837, Cambridge, 1930, p. 83.

48 *Painting and The Fine Arts: being the Articles under those Heads contributed to the Seventh Edition of the Encyclopædia Britannica*, B. R. Haydon and William Hazlitt, Edinburgh, 1838, pp. 213–4. [1830.]

49 C. R. Leslie, *A Hand-Book for Young Painters*, London, 1853, pp. 137–8.

50 Blake, *ed. cit.*, p. 911.

51 Thomas Smith, *Recollections of the British Institution*, London, 1860, p. 108.

52 *Autobiographical Notes of the Life of William Bell Scott*, ed. W. Minto, London, 1892, i, 162–4. If I can obtain enough material I hope to deal with von Holst at a later date.

53 *Essays and Criticisms by Thomas Griffiths Wainewright*, ed. W. Carew Hazlitt, London, 1880, p. 202. See also Jonathan Curling, *Janus Weathercock*, London, 1938.

54 *The Farington Diary*, iii, 91.

55 Presumably the painting, 102 × 95 cm., now in a private collection at Basle.

56 Now in the collection of Professor Dr. Paul Ganz, Basle; 63 × 76 cm.

[57] Letter to George Richmond, 1 June 1874; from a transcript kindly lent to me by Mr. Geoffrey Grigson.

[58] Formerly in the collection of the Countess of Guildford, who bought all Fuseli's remaining drawings, and later in that of Sir Hugh Walpole.

[59] *Dante Gabriel Rossetti: His Family Letters with a Memoir*, ed. W. M. Rossetti, London, 1895, i, 117.

[60] See W. M. Rossetti, *Preraphaelite Diaries and Letters*, London, 1900, p. 176.

[61] Professor Dr. Paul Ganz's *Die Zeichnungen Johann Heinrich Füsslis* will appear shortly. I have to acknowledge my gratitude to Professor Ganz for much kindness in giving me photographs and catalogues unobtainable in England.

[62] Especially in *Narrative Pictures*, London, 1937, and *Splendours and Miseries*, London, 1943.

[63] *Henry Fuseli, R.A.*, 1741–1825, John Piper, *Signature*, London, 10, 1938, p. 14.

[64] The Duchess of Sermoneta, *The Locks of Norbury*, London, 1940, pp. 46–7.

[65] *The Farington Diary*, ii, 45.

[66] *Alte Handzeichnungen des XV–XVIII Jahrhunderts aus der Sammlung Arnold Otto Meyers*, C. G. Boerner, Leipzig, March 19–20, 1914, lot 256.

[67] Smith, *Nollekens and his times*, ed. cit., ii, 418. In the 1810 edition of Pilkington's *Dictionary of Artists*, p. 467, under Alexander Runciman, Fuseli refers to 'John Brown, celebrated for design', as being Runciman's friend.

[68] Knowles, *op. cit.*, i, 37.

[69] James L. Caw, *Scottish Painting Past and Present*, 1620–1908, Edinburgh and London, 1908, p. 41.

[70] Knowles, *op. cit.*, i, 396.

[71] *Ibid.*, iii, 80; *Aphorism* 55.

[72] *Ibid.*, iii, 87; *Aphorism* 78.

[73] *Ibid.*, iii, 145; *Aphorism* 231.

[74] *Splendours and Miseries*, pp. 226–7.

THE IMAGINATION OF
JOHN MARTIN

EACH generation sets up its standards by which it proceeds to judge the works of art of its own day and of the
past; too often these standards become a yardstick with
which to measure a picture, to justify the declaration that
this falls short of the obscure ideal by some thirty-five
inches, or that that contrives to approach within a few
centimetres of the indeterminate goal.

Although the criticism of one art in the terms of
another is to be deprecated, it is difficult to see why
painting should require higher or more essentially purist
standards than those expressed for poetry by Mr.
Geoffrey Grigson when he wrote 'Illuminations cannot
be faked; and as I have declared, the excellence of a
genuine lyric or a long poem does not degrade the
different excellence for a different purpose, of a successful, and really funny limerick . . . *Orpheus, Eurydice,
Hermes* [R. M. Rilke], and *Miss Twye* [Gavin Ewart] are
for different occasions, or different states of mind, not
different readers. The time is . . . over for arguing that
one *is* poetry and the other is not.'[1]

If a painting is a genuine work, and not a mere
fashionable *plat du jour* pastiche, then that painting deserves
consideration divorced from any preconceptions of what
a work of art *should* or *must* be; it deserves a recognition
and an examination unhampered by undue concentration
upon its adherence to, or deviation from, a current set
of rules.

There is no reason for us to follow the example of the
contemporary critics who damned Turner for not being
Claude, any more than there is reason that we should
praise Turner at the expense of Claude, as Ruskin did
in the first edition of the first volume of *Modern Painters*,

1843. Incidentally, it is only fair to add that Ruskin regretted this, and justified it in a letter to Samuel Prout, written before he had acknowledged the identity of the 'Graduate of Oxford', where he says, 'My friend has been much cramped in his work by the fear of injuring living painters. I know that the really *sore* point with him is not that *Claude* should be put above Turner, but that *Stanfield* and *Creswick* should. But deliberately to sit down in order to prove the superiority of a man who has made his £100,000, over those who are struggling up the hill, however he might wish to do so, would have been, I think, an ungenerous step.'²

John Martin was set up by over-exuberant critics as a rival to Turner, and he never seems to have been forgiven for failing to treat this supposed rivalry seriously, or showing an ambition to imitate the older artist in his strictly personal development.

Martin has been summarily condemned because his pictures do not fit into the elaborately carved and gilded frame of the recognized manner, or because his subjects and his treatment of them do not please the sensitized good taste of the critic. They are 'triumphs of Perspective in paint and the Mechanical Sublime,—are monuments also of the vulgar passion for novelty which seemed to raise them to the rank of European masterpieces, and lessons how brief the fame is, which rests on fashion and singularity without truth. For these pictures are false in every vital point; . . . No painting so untrue can ever win its way deep, or touch us long; not if the artist "mingles earth with sea, and sea with sky" in his colossal commonplace.'³ Thackeray, whose level as an art-critic can be seen in his perpetual schoolboy sniggers at Etty's nudes, wrote, 'Martin I would venture to place in the theatrical heroic class of artists. One looks at these strange pieces and wonders how people can be found to admire, and yet they do. Grave old people, with chains and seals,

look dumbfounded into those vast perspectives and think
that the apex of the sublime is reached there.'[4]

The last three paintings executed by John Martin,
The Great Day of His Wrath (now in the Tate Gallery),
The Last Judgment (in the possession of Rex C. Nan
Kivell, Esq.) and *The Plains of Heaven* (in the possession
of Lady Harris) were exhibited all over England in the
years following his death and enjoyed a success unequalled by any similar venture. How widely they must
have travelled and how well known they must have been we
can see from the evidence of the best-seller, *East Lynne*,
where they are employed for emotive purposes as being
within the terms of reference understood by the general
public, 'We went to Lynneborough to see Martin's
pictures of the Last Judgment. . . . There were three large
pictures. One was called the 'Plains of Heaven', and I
liked that the best; and we all did. Oh, you should have
seen it! . . . There was a river, you know, and boats,
beautiful gondolas they looked, taking the redeemed to the
shores of heaven. They were shadowy figures in white
robes, myriads and myriads of them, for they reached all
up in the air to the holy city; it seemed to be in the clouds,
coming down from God. The flowers grew on the banks of
the river, pink and blue and violet; all colours, but so bright
and beautiful; brighter than our flowers are here.'[5]

Haydon recognized the difficulty of appreciating
Martin when he wrote of him and Francis Danby, whose
paintings of *The Opening of the Sixth Seal* (National
Gallery of Eire, Dublin), and *The Israelites crossing the Red
Sea* were frankly competitive, that they were 'men of
extraordinary imagination, but infants in painting. These
pictures always seem to artists as if a child of extraordinary fancy had taken up a brush to express its invention. The public, who are no judges of the art as an art,
overpraise their inventions, and the artists, who are always
professional, see only the errors of the brush.'[6]

34. John Martin. Viaduct leading to Sezincourt House

Any attempt to understand John Martin must take into account the family into which he was born on 19 July 1789. The fourth son of a jack-of-all-trades of nomadic habits, temporarily settled at Haydon Bridge, near Hexham, Northumberland, he lived all his life in the shadow of the toppling tower of lunacy.

His eldest brother, William Martin, printed upwards of two hundred pamphlets on his inventions, his life and his philosophy. That some of his inventions were practical we know from the fact that he was awarded a medal in 1813 by the Society of Arts for an improvement in the mechanism of the spring weighing-machine; further, his safety lamp was not only seriously considered as a rival to that of Sir Humphry Davy by a Select Committee of the House of Commons, but was also the subject of a report by four wastemen at Willington Colliery who found that it was brighter, cheaper, safer and burned longer than the Davy lamp.[7]

It seems probable that William Martin's attitude to his inventions was rather similar to that of Robert Hooke in the seventeenth century. Most of Hooke's acrimony against those whom he accused of stealing his inventions was caused by the fact that his brain teemed with ideas which he noted down and never developed, so that when they were expanded by someone else he quite genuinely felt that he was, in fact, the original begetter of the schemes. Such, it seems, was Martin's attitude to the ventilation of mines, larger wheels for railways, iron rails and the High Level bridge across the Tyne, erected by the younger Stephenson. In his pamphlets he continually refers to ideas thrown off in conversation with friends many years before which have been 'stolen' by others.

As a philosopher William Martin was an anti-Newtonian who continued to believe that light was the mystic dwelling-place of God, and to disregard the evidence supplied by Robert Boyle that air was a body, possessing weight.[8] Some idea of his opinions can be gathered from the titles of his pamphlets, one of which reads 'WILLIAM MARTIN, PHILOSOPHICAL CONQUEROR OF ALL NATIONS. Also A Challenge for all College Professors, To prove this wrong and themselves right, and that Air is not the first great Cause of all things, animate and inanimate. I say boldly that it is the Spirit of God, and God himself, as the Scripture says God is a Spirit, and that Spirit was never created or made, or how could there be any Creation? This is clear to anyone that has common Sense. *Printed by M. Ross, 48 Pilgrim Street, Newcastle.* February 1846.' By the time he published this pamphlet William had given up all pretensions to sanity and the inventions of his earlier years had been more or less forgotten by all save himself and his brother John. He walked about the streets of Newcastle with his breast hung with an immense home-made gong, a decoration bestowed by himself for his contributions to science and philosophy; on his head he wore a helmet of tortoise-shell, mounted and bound in brass.

When William Bell Scott was introduced to him in 1845, he 'with exaggerated politeness, drew his feet together, bent forward, lifted his tortoise-shell hat high in the air, and answered, "Gratified to meet you, sir! I am the philosophical conqueror of all nations, that is what I am!"' Bell Scott goes on to say that while 'he was manifestly crazed, yet he had that about him that made one treat him with respect. A noble presence even was his, although he was poor enough to sell his pamphlets thus on the street, which pamphlets were of course only evidence of his craze.'[9]

Of the second brother, Richard, comparatively little is known beyond the fact that he served for twenty-nine years in the army, was present at the battle of Waterloo, and finally rose to the rank of Quartermaster-Sergeant in the Grenadier Guards. According to John, he wrote

pamphlets on the subject of Perpetual Motion, which he
sent to well-known public figures, mentioning his relationship with the celebrated painter but neglecting to pre-pay
the postage.

In spite of this statement, credited to John, it is doubtful
if there is not some confusion here as the inventor of
the system of Perpetual Motion was William, while no
such pamphlets by Richard can be found. Further,
postage-due from Wallsend or Newcastle in those days
would have amounted to a considerable sum, while
postage from one part of London to another would not
have amounted to sufficient to impress itself upon John's
mind, and Richard lived in London.

In 1830 he published a book of poems[10] which
contained a frontispiece by his brother and which were
presumably printed at his expense. Unfortunately these
poems show none of the fantastic vision of John or of the
eccentricity of William, but are 'literate and thoroughly
pedestrian'.[11]

The third brother, Jonathan, achieved greater notoriety,
for, having announced his intention publicly, on 1 February
1829, he secreted himself after the service in York Minster
and started a fire as a protest against the godforsaken
profligacy of the clergy. This fire consumed a hundred and
thirty-one feet of the main roof, from the east end to the
lantern tower. Captured without much difficulty, Jonathan
was defended at the Yorkshire Spring Assizes by Lord
Brougham, at the expense of his brother. He was found to
be guilty but insane. After his removal to Bedlam he was
visited by the anonymous author (tentatively identified by
Miss Mona Wilson[12] as R. C. Smith or 'Merlinus
Anglicus, Jun.') of *Bits of Biography: Blake, the Vision Seer,
and Martin, The York Minster Incendiary*,[13] an article which,
by the way, was responsible, through a French translator's
making one character from Blake and Martin, for the
nineteenth-century rumour that the former had spent some

time in Bedlam. When seen, Jonathan was contentedly
engaged in drawing a seven-headed bishop rushing into
the jaws of an enormous crocodile.

Before his indulgence in the act which cost him his
liberty for the rest of his life, Jonathan too had given
way to the family weakness for print and autobiography
in a pamphlet of which I transcribe the elaborate title-page
of the third edition: 'THE LIFE OF JONATHAN
MARTIN, of Darlington, Tanner, Written by Himself.
Containing An Account of the Extraordinary Inter-
positions of Divine Providence on his behalf during a
period of six years' service in the Navy, including his
wonderful escapes in the Action of Copenhagen, and in
many affairs on the Coasts of Spain and Portugal, in
Egypt, &c. Also, an Account of the Embarkation of the
British Army after the Battle of Corunna. Likewise an
Account of his subsequent Conversion and Christian
Experience, with the Persecutions he suffered for Con-
science' sake, being locked up in an asylum and ironed,
describing his miraculous Escape through the roof of
the house, having first ground off his Fetters with a
Sandy Stone. His Singular Dreams of the Destruction of
London, and the Host of Armed Men overrunning
England, also of the Son of Buonaparte taking England,
&c. &c. To which is added—A Letter from Mr.
Fletcher, on the prophecies concerning the latter times.
Mark! my kind readers, the hand of God in a poor
humble cot, God has raised of us four brothers; my oldest
brother he has made a Natural Philosopher, my youngest,
an Historical Painter, his drawings and engravings has
made Kings and Emperors to wonder. The Emperor of
Russia at this time has made him a present of a diamond
ring, but I, the unworthiest, God has given to me the gift
of prophecy, which is the best of all, for I feel that God
is with me. *Lincoln: printed for and sold by the Author, by
R. E. Leary*, 1828. Price Sixpence.'[14] The blue paper

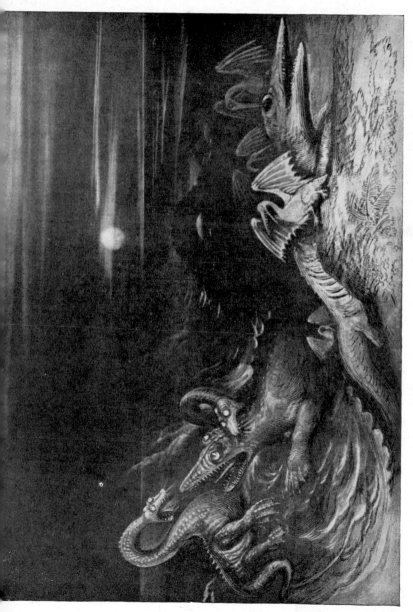

36. John Martin. The Sea-Dragons as they Lived

37a. JOHN MARTIN. The Crucifixion

37b. JOHN MARTIN. The Last Judgment

38a. JOHN MARTIN. Belshazzar's Feast

38b. WILLIAM MARTIN. Belshazzar's Feast

40. John Martin. The Deluge

42. John Martin. Satan Presiding at the Infernal Council

43. JOHN MARTIN. Manfred on the Jungfrau

wrapper of this remarkable production bears a notice which reads, 'N.B. Gentlemen and Ladies, think it not strange that I charge you one shilling for my Book and the Price on the title only sixpence for the Lord says remember the Poor. You will find my Book give you satisfaction.'

In spite of this background of eccentricity and irresponsibility, some of the mud from which stuck to him in the form of the nickname of 'Mad Martin', John Martin managed to retain his balance, however precarious it must have seemed on occasions like that, in March 1838, when Ralph Thomas noted that 'Mrs. Martin came here on Monday. Oh, what a state of anxiety and distress he is in! Martin, she fears, may go out of his mind, and she is afraid to speak to him. As to herself, she says his conduct will lead her to do what he will be surprised at, for she cannot endure much longer such distress and anxiety. He is sullen and will not speak to her or anybody.' [15]

Later in the same year an event happened which might easily have deranged Martin, for his brother Jonathan's son, Richard, who lived with him, became obsessed with the idea that he had contracted typhus and that his breath was turning those around him black, and he committed suicide. By this time, however, John Martin had begun to rid himself of his intense preoccupations of the previous ten years and, with these filling only a part of his mind, had once more started to paint.

Of these preoccupations referred to, the principal one was an ambitious effort to secure a better and a purer water supply for London, an effort in support of which Martin produced several pamphlets at dates between 1828 and 1849. In these pamphlets he was among the first to propound many ideas which have since been adopted, although he has never received any credit as the originator of them. Incidental to the plans regarding the purer water supply was the question of the disposal of sewage for, in 1836, the Select Committee appointed to

examine Martin's plan had declared in their report that
'The Thames, to this day, receives the excrementious
matter from nearly a million and a half of human beings;
the washing of their foul linen; the filth and refuse of
many hundred manufactories; the offal and decomposing
vegetable substances from the markets, the foul and gory
liquid from the slaughter-houses, and the purulent abomi-
nations from hospitals and dissecting rooms, too disgusting
to detail. Thus that most noble river, which has been given
to us by Providence for our health, recreation, and
beneficial use, is converted into the Common Sewer of
London, and the sickening mixture it contains is daily
pumped up into the water as a common beverage for the
inhabitants of the most civilized capital in Europe.'[16]

Martin's plan was that the sewage of London should
be salvaged and used as manure, a plan which, with all
its implications, should be re-examined by those who
today are agitating against this extraordinarily short-
sighted waste of valuable material, a wastage to which
Erasmus Darwin had already drawn attention, although he
went further than Martin in his suggestion that church
burial-grounds should be abolished and the decomposed
bodies used for the enrichment of the soil.[17]

Of course, Martin's scheme would need to undergo a
certain amount of revision, particularly with regard to the
treatment of the manure, as it has been found that today,
as a result of the changes in the standard of living, human
sewage is only too apt to produce a crop of first-rate
tomatoes without the necessity of sowing any seed.[18]
Martin founded the Metropolitan Sewage Manure Company and managed to obtain recognition for it by means
of an Act of Parliament. The undertaking failed not on
account of any impracticability of its avowed intentions,
but merely because the directors of the Company disagreed
upon so many fundamental principles, disagreements with
which Martin deals in one of his pamphlets.[19]

In addition to his elaborate and sensible plans for improving not only the health but also the amenities of London, Martin produced a series of inventions, including an Elastic Iron Ship, a New Principle of Steam Navigation, an Elastic Chain Cable, Coast Lights on a New Construction, and a Plan for Purifying the Air and Preventing Explosion in Coal Mines.[20]

No doubt some of these inventions were as fantastic and impracticable as those of William after he had crossed the frontier from mere eccentricity into frank insanity, but from a letter written by Martin to Prince Albert in December 1852, it would seem that the Board of Trinity House had 'erected several Lighthouses on the principle I proposed and yet both deny me compensation and evade recognition of my claim to the invention'.[21] There is also the fact that Martin's plan for coal mines, which he had improved from a suggestion made by his brother William many years earlier, was produced before the Select Parliamentary Committee on Accidents in Mines in 1835, where it was rejected, not on account of its impracticability, but only because the Davy lamp, though not safer, was cheaper.[22] Those who drew a handsome royalty from the accident of coal having been found beneath their inherited estates could turn a blind eye to the deaths of miners, but could not be expected to permit anything which might decrease, even for a short time, their fortuitous dividends; all of Martin's struggles, on behalf of his inventions and schemes, with vested interests assume an extraordinary vividness today.

Unfortunately the loss or destruction of Ralph Thomas's *Journal* makes it very difficult to form anything like a proper idea of Martin's religious beliefs, although an understanding of these would be of inestimable value in attempting to comprehend the formation of his imagination as it is displayed in his paintings.

Thomas tells us that 'Martin is a thorough Deist and believes that all good flows from a God. But he entirely

disbelieves that anything not good, merciful, or great
can come from such a source', [23] and it is obvious that
Thomas was at times deeply shocked by his friend's
opinions, as on the occasions when Martin told him that
'geology taught us that we could not calculate, but it was
clear the world was millions of years old and would
continue growing older for millions of years to come', [24]
and that the world was originally 'peopled with inferior
animals, then a grade superior, and finally with man. This
I thought ridiculous enough, but he said he got it all from
geology; for there were no bones to be found of man,
though there were the bones of all sorts of other animals.' [25]

We have a considerable amount of information on
Martin's connections with the geologists, some of which
will be mentioned later. Apart from that there is a reference
to a visit from Martin and one of his daughters to Gideon
Mantell, probably the most distinguished English geological contemporary of Dean William Buckland, who
writes of him as 'the celebrated, most justly celebrated,
artist, whose wonderful conceptions are the finest produc-
tions of modern art. Mr. Martin was deeply interested in
the remains of the Iguanodon etc. I wish I could induce
him to portray the country of the Iguanodon: no other
pencil but his should attempt such a subject.' [26] That
Mantell managed to persuade the artist can be seen in his
book, *The Wonders of Geology*, 1838, where the subject
appears as a mezzotint frontispiece to the first volume,
possibly engraved by the artist's son Alfred. Another
more magnificent plate of a similar subject is one of
The Sea-Dragons as they lived, mezzotinted by the artist
himself as the frontispiece to a most amusing and almost
forgotten work, Thomas Hawkins's *The Book of the Great
Sea-Dragons*, 1840. This book, which is dedicated to Dean
Buckland, presumably to soften the hard remarks about
him in the text, is a curious mixture of scientific thought
with religious fervour which must have appealed to

44. John Martin. Marcus Curtius

45. John Martin. Distant View of London

Martin, many of whose own writings show so much of the same spirit.

There is evidence, however, that Martin's unorthodox ideas did not stop with this acceptance of the theory of evolution; this is fragmentary but, I think, conclusive. There is a contemporary record that 'Mr. Martin had some singular notions on the subject of Religion, and was concerned with a man named Ussher in the publication of a paraphrase on the Psalms, which were published about the year 1831 or 2 in octavo'.[27] I have so far failed to trace a copy of this book which must be of considerable interest in view of Ralph Thomas's statement that 'According to Martin, David was "a cruel monster", and he denied that he could have been a man "after God's own heart". "David took the merit of this title to himself", he said, "just as Henry VIII called himself 'Defender of the Faith'!" '[28] The other hint which I have found is also concerned with a still unlocated book. This is an advertisement in a pamphlet in my possession,[29] which reads, 'Shortly will be published, The Gathering Standard of the World, seen in the British Flag. The Threefold Banner—Cross of the Holy Bible, The Ensign of Messiah's Coming. With Designs by J. Martin.' As it is most improbable that the illustrations to a pamphlet of this nature would have been an ordinary commercial undertaking, it would seem that Martin was in some way connected with the movement known as the British-Israelites, founded by the naval lieutenant Richard Brothers, according to which the inhabitants of these islands are representatives of the lost tribes of the Old Testament.

Martin's reliance on the Bible involved him in the subject of the chronology of the book of *Genesis* as deeply as Bishop Ussher. We can see this in his note in his description of his engraving of *The Deluge* where he justifies the inclusion of Methuselah in the scene, 'Now, the age of Methuselah, when he begat Lamech, and the age of Lamech, when he begat Noah, added together, and that product deducted from Methuselah's extreme age, demonstrates that that ancient patriarch lived in the year of the Flood, and lived till his grandson Noah was 600 years old; for Noah had not, it appears, completed his 600th year when he entered the Ark; consequently the oldest man perished in the Flood.'[30]

That he was also familiar with seventeenth-century speculation upon the causes of the Deluge is shown by his reference to Thomas Burnet who, in his *The Theory of the Earth*, 1684–9, 'imagines that all the waters now upon its surface were confined within its centre, being covered with a thick crust which constituted the Superficial world. By the Supernatural Commotion of the doomed planet at the period of the Universal Deluge, he supposes this shell to have given way, and an impulse being imparted to the central waters, they rushed up from the receptacle in which they had been confined, and overspread the whole surface of the globe.'[31]

But, a man of the nineteenth century interested and involved in invention and the friend of geologists and scientists, Martin could not accept the word of the scriptural speculator without question but had to support his imagination with the reasoned arguments of the astronomers. So he told Ralph Thomas, on 17 February 1834, that 'Baron Cuvier came to see me when he was in London, on account of my having, in my *Deluge*, made the event the consequence of sun, moon and comet in conjunction; the moon and comet drawing the water over the earth. This was Cuvier's opinion, he told me so, and he expressed himself highly pleased that I had entertained the same notion.'[32]

William Martin did not always agree with his brother's interpretations of the Divine scriptures and expressed his own feelings on the subject of the Flood and on geology in a pamphlet entitled 'The Christian Philosopher's explanation of the General Deluge, and the Proper Cause of all the different Strata; wherein it is clearly demonstrated, that One Deluge was the Cause of the Whole, which divinely proves that God is not a Liar, but that the Bible is strictly true. *Newcastle: printed by W. Fordyce, 48, Dean Street.* 1834.' A further amusing piece of evidence relating to William's disapproval of his brother's ideas is an engraving in my possession of *Belshazzar's Feast*, lettered 'Mezzotinto first Engraved on Tin Plates by W^m. Martin NP. Wallsend. 1831'.[33] This production by the Natural Philosopher is a copy of John's engraving, with the addition of a rocket-like object, representing the actual hand writing on the wall, a piece of detail missing in the original.

The kind of painting with which we always associate Martin's name was not, as it might seem today, looked upon by his contemporaries as completely outside the general current of the time. There were other painters in the same genre of whom the best known is Francis Danby, and a note in one of Beddoes's letters suggests that, perhaps, the interchange between Danby and Martin was not so completely one sided as has been assumed. In this letter Beddoes asks Bryan Waller Proctor, 'Have you seen Martin's Deluge; do you like it? And do you know that it is a rascally plagiarism upon Danby? D. was to have painted a picture for the King: subject the opening of ye sixth seal in ye revelations: price 800 guineas: he had collected his ideas and scene, and very imprudently mentioned them publicly to his friends & foes—it appears; . . . and lo! his own ideas stare at him out of Martin's canvas at the institution.'[34]

Another aspect of Martin's influence that has never been properly examined is his connection with certain American romantic painters, notably Thomas Cole and Washington Allston. In the case of the latter we have some information on the connection, in the progress of which Allston became the centre of a story which, it has been said, 'is a far greater Romantic fantasy, in the contemporary, Surrealist sense of the term' [35] than anything he actually wrote or painted.

This is the record of his vast painting, about twelve by sixteen feet, of *Belshazzar's Feast*. Allston had almost completed the picture when he returned to America from London in 1819, and shortly before he had shown it to his friend Martin, who had not agreed with him about his conception of the subject. Returning home Martin produced a sketch showing his own ideas of the Feast and, displaying it to Allston, found that he had no objections to his carrying it out. As the theme lay smouldering in his mind, the winds of Martin's imagination gently fanned it into a fire, and he became increasingly enthusiastic about the subject and finally painted the picture which, on its exhibition at the British Institution in 1821, as he himself said, caused 'more noise than any picture ever did before'.[36]

It was an immediate and overwhelming success; so dense were the crowds that thronged to see it that it had to be specially railed off, to protect it from the enthusiastic crush, and because of its presence the exhibition remained open for an extra three weeks. The picture was bought for a thousand guineas by Collins, for whom Martin had earlier worked as a painter on china, and was exhibited at his shop in the Strand, with a transparency of it in the window to attract the attention of the passer-by, and, in addition, the directors of the British Institution awarded the painter a premium of two hundred pounds. It was generally praised by the critics and even the painters were forced to admire the success of the *tour de force*, although the ill-drawing of some of the figures and the unconventionality of the colouring were remarked upon. The most notable of the adverse critics was Charles Lamb to whom the idea of the *littleness* of man was deeply and constitutionally repugnant and even he admitted Martin's astonishing imagination while attempting to justify his own dislike and fear;[37] Lamb, it will be realized, was in opposition to Martin, for whom 'Newton's authority was squarely behind that view of the cosmos which saw in man a puny, irrelevant spectator (so far as a being wholly imprisoned in a dark room can be called such) of the vast mathematical system whose regular motions according to mechanical principles constituted the world of nature'.[38]

Allston's painting, on the other hand, never reached completion. For more than twenty-five years, living at Cambridgeport, Massachusetts, he gradually worked his way back from the almost finished picture to the bare canvas, at one time even taking the advice of Gilbert Stuart to alter the perspective so that the whole surface of the painting became a network with 'more than twenty thousand chalk-lines in circles and arcs, to bring the amended figures into correct drawing'.[39] During these years *Belshazzar's Feast* became a hell in which the painter had been condemned to live. He even demanded that workmen going into his studio should enter with their backs to it, and he believed that he was destined to survive until it was finished, so that when he died, in 1843, one of his friends could note with relief that 'he had escaped that terrible vision—the nightmare, the incubus, the tormentor of his life—his unfinished picture'.[40]

Martin's first success in the genre with which we now associate his name, which John Cawse, the animal painter, described as 'The feo faw fum style',[41] was *Joshua commanding the Sun to stand still*, exhibited at the Royal Academy in 1816, where it prompted a writer to prophesy that his name 'will never appear in another catalogue without the addenda of Academic honours to which this picture has so wonderfully entitled him. On any such honours his genius will reflect honour.'[42] However, in 1814, Martin had arrived at the opening of the

Academy to find that some anonymous Academician had contrived, on the varnishing day, to spill a thick stream of dark varnish right down the centre of his painting of *Clytie*. Although Benjamin West sent his son to apologize, Martin was not satisfied and he developed a dislike of the Academy which never lessened, and which was probably responsible for the fact that when he was proposed for an Associateship in 1820 he received no support.[43]

Apart from this quarrel there is no doubt that Martin agreed with Bulwer's declaration 'that the Royal Academy was intended for the encouragement of historical paintings —that it is filled with landscapes and portraits; that it was intended to incorporate and to cheer on all distinguished students—that it has excluded and persecuted many of the greatest we possess, and that at this moment, sixty-five years after its establishment, our greatest living artists, with scarcely any exceptions, have *not* been educated at an academy, intended of course *to* educate genius, even more than to support it afterwards! With the assumption of a public body, it has combined the exclusiveness of a private clique.'[44] Constable, who had received tardy and grudging recognition from the Academy himself and who knew the value of such belated attention, approved of Martin's making no effort to canvass his way into this exclusive club and said, 'John Martin looked at the Royal Academy from the Plains of Nineveh'.[45]

It was natural that his antagonism should turn Martin towards the British Institution, and he was strengthened in his support of that body when in 1817, *Joshua*, which the Academy had hung in an anteroom, was awarded a premium of a hundred pounds. It seems possible that there may have been some personal pique on behalf of one of his own friends in J. C. Meade's suggestion to Farington that the funds had been 'applied from *favouritism*',[46] for no such suggestion is conveyed in any of the contemporary newspaper notices I have seen.

It is further of interest to note that Martin was one of the group of artists responsible for the foundation of the Society of British Artists in 1823, a society which was immediately designed as a rival to the monopoly of the Royal Academy, and that, in 1836, he was one of those who gave evidence against the older body before the Select Parliamentary Committee.

Although Martin exhibited any picture which he expected to be widely discussed, at the British Institution, he did not cut himself off from the Royal Academy but continued to exhibit there throughout his life, showing, for the most part, these romantic landscapes with which he, Danby and Allston, escaped from the terrors of their imaginative worlds. It is interesting to note that, even in his landscapes, man remained for Martin a diminutive figure, and that the trees are unduly large in proportion to those under them.

The success of his scriptural subject paintings assured Martin of popularity, but it was a popularity which might well have remained local for, until after his death, most of his paintings were exhibited only in London, although a few might have been seen occasionally at the Liverpool Academy and elsewhere, so that as a rule the provinces and the continent of Europe would have known him only from the articles which appeared from time to time in periodicals, such as the *Library of the Fine Arts*, and from the little steel-engravings by E. Finden, W. R. Smith, E. Challis and others which appeared in the various annuals, *Forget Me Not*, *Friendship's Offering*, *The Keepsake*, *The Literary Souvenir* and so on, between 1827 and 1837. However, Martin himself was interested in engraving, his first publication being 'Characters of Trees in a series of seven plates drawn and etched by F. [*sic*] Martin, landscape-painter to H.R.H. the Princess Charlotte and H.S.H. the Prince of Saxe-Coburg, R. Ackermann, 1817', and the substitution of steel for copper-plates in the process of mezzotint engraving, which occurred in 1823, appealed to him immediately, both as an artist and as an ingenious mechanic involved in inventions and improvements.

The principal trouble about copper had been its comparative softness, although it must be remembered that the copper-plate up to the nineteenth century was harder than that of today, being beaten and not rolled. As a result of this softness the 'burr' on the plate soon wore down, under the strain of printing, and the mezzotint quickly lost that velvety blackness upon which its attraction depends. The introduction of the steel-plate meant that, from being a process for the production of a necessarily limited edition, the mezzotint became a method for reproducing works intended to have a wide circulation. By the end of 1824 Martin had already published two small plates in the new medium, both wholly successful.

So far as I know John Martin is the only artist of any reputation or standing who has seriously adopted mezzotint as a medium of self-expression, although certainly George Stubbs had made some use of it, for it is usually looked upon as a method of reproduction only. Although Martin did employ the medium largely in its reproductive capacity to increase and satisfy the public demand for his best-known paintings, he also designed many of his subjects directly on to the plate, as in the case of his twenty-four illustrations of *Paradise Lost*, 1825–7, and the twenty *Illustrations of the Bible*, 1831–5.

It was his engraved work that brought Martin European fame, and brought him also £20,000 in the course of a few years. Unfortunately, his very success proved to be its own undoing, for, in 1836, giving evidence before the Fine Arts Commission, Martin had to testify that the activities of pirate-engravers had forced him to curtail his own practice to an extent where it had become practically non-existent. This was a great misfortune, for the

46. JOHN MARTIN. The Last Man

47. John Martin. The Destruction of Sodom and Gomorrah

endless pains he took in the preparation and inking of his plates, in his own printing establishment behind his house in Allsop Terrace, Marylebone, had results which can only be fully appreciated by placing one of his own engravings beside a piracy of the same subject.

The greater number of the few oil paintings by Martin which I have been able to trace have become so dark and dirty with inattention and age that they cannot be reproduced to give any idea of their original state, so that we are forced to rely upon such of his engravings as we can find to form an opinion of his work. The use of these engravings is not, as would be the case of some artist's works, a grave disadvantage so far as Martin is concerned, for, as I have said, he engraved them himself and Blake said 'No one can finish so high as the original inventor'.[47] Further it is at least possible that the works appear to greater advantage in the engraved form. The paintings, some of which are as large as nine by thirteen feet, are inclined to be so complex and over-populated that it is almost impossible for the eye to take them in as a whole, while the simplification and compression incident to the engraving seems to have given them a greater unity.

No longer are the technical flaws so evident or distracting as they appear to have been found by the contemporary critics who wrote 'It may be questioned whether it is within the scope of painting to express that which Mr. Martin has attempted, but there can be no doubt that he has displayed very extraordinary and original powers, and that his production, *in spite of rules*, is a highly interesting one',[48] or 'the painter may, perhaps, have in some instances disregarded a few of the technicalities of art; . . . the interest of the spectator . . . will perhaps be somewhat lessened by the coarse colouring of some of its groupes'.[49]

That Martin was a literary painter, an illustrator, does not seem to me to be sufficient reason for ignoring him; if the anti-literature standard was to be applied logically and completely the history of English painting might be given in a few pages, though these pages would be so dull as to be almost unreadable.

As a man Martin seems to have been the possessor of great personal charm in spite of a hasty temper, and Frith says that he was 'certainly one of the most beautiful human beings I ever beheld'.[50] He was intimate with Haydon, who was painting his *Pharaoh dismissing Moses and Aaron* when 'Martin called and thought I wanted more space. That fellow should have wings. He is an extraordinary genius in his way. He expressed himself much delighted, but wanted a tower ten thousand feet high, and a hall or two in which a man might take a bed before he got to the end of the room; where when a party was given a man must dispatch a courier with relays for soup or fish, if they happened to be at the bottom of the table.'[51] Haydon's pupil, William Bewick, gives a description of Martin's appearance about 1823; he 'was of about middle size—fair, extremely good-looking and pleasing in his expression; there was nothing remarkable or eccentric in his appearance; he was smart and trim, well dressed and gentlemanly, and when seen out of doors he seemed to delight in a light primrose-coloured vest with bright metal buttons, a blue coat set off with the same, his hair carefully curled, and shining with macassar oil. He was prepossessing, with a great flow of conversation and argument. He was also imaginative, and kept to his points with a tenacity not easily subdued.'[52]

In spite of his friendship we find Haydon as acute as ever when it comes to criticizing from the professional point of view. He says, 'Martin has a curious picture of the Creation—God creating the Sun and the Moon, which is a total failure from his ignorance of the associations and habits of the mind.

'No being in a human shape has ever exceeded eight feet. Therefore to put a human being with a hand extended, and a large shining circular flat body not much larger than the thing shaped like a human hand and four fingers, and call that body the sun, makes one laugh; for no effort can get over the idea that it is not larger than a hand. And the Creator, so far from being grand, looks no larger than a human being, and the sun looks like a shilling. It can't be otherwise, and no association can ever get over the relative proportions of a hand, and what is not bigger than a hand. It is no use to say that hand is a mile long. No effort of the mind can entertain such a notion: besides, it is the grossest of all gross ideas to make the power and essence of the Creator depend on size. His nature might be comprehended in an ordinary-sized brain, and it is vulgar to make Him striding across a horizon, and say the horizon is fifty miles long. It is contrary to human experience, and the Creator, so far from looking large, makes the horizon look little; for this is a natural result when a being with legs, arms, hands, beard, face is seen stretching across it. When Martin diminished his buildings to a point, put specks for human beings, then there was no improbability that his rooms might be, for aught we know, forty miles long, his doors six miles high, his windows a mile across, or his second floor two miles and three-quarters above his first floor—tight work for the servants if they slept in the attics. They must have had depots of night-candles by the way. Martin, in looking at his Babylon with a friend of mine, said: "I mean that tower to be seven miles high". The association is preposterous. There is nothing grand in a man stepping from York to Lancaster; but when he makes a great Creator fifteen inches, paints a sun the size of a bank token, draws a line for the sea, and makes one leg of God in it, and the other above, and says, "There! That horizon is twenty miles long, and therefore God's leg must be sixteen relatively to the horizon", the artist really deserves as much pity as the poorest maniac in Bedlam.'[53]

It seems probable that Haydon gave Martin his blunt opinion on this picture, for it is one of the very few occasions known to me on which a figure dwarfs a landscape or a building. We can see how accurately Martin worked out his proportions from his pamphlet on his painting of *Belshazzar's Feast* [54] where, from the size of one figure, he demonstrates that the hall is a mile in length.

Martin's works appealed largely to the writers of his time, including Bulwer who, Mr. Michael Sadleir suggests, had something in common with the painter.[55] Bulwer wrote of him that he was 'the greatest, the most lofty, the most permanent, the most original genius of his age . . . he has made the *Old* Testament, with its stern traditionary grandeur—its solemn shadows and ancestral terrors—his own element and appanage . . . Vastness is his sphere, yet he has not lost or circumfused his genius in its space; he has chained, and wielded and measured it, at his will; he has transfused its character into narrow limits; he has compassed the Infinite itself with mathematical precision . . . Alone and guideless, he has penetrated the remote caverns of the past, and gazed on the primeval shapes of the gone world.' [56]

In addition to this eulogy, there is an interesting note in a copy of *Illustrations of the Old and New Testaments by Westall and Martin*, 1837, where W. M. Rossetti attests to the high opinion he and his brother had of the imaginative quality of Martin's work, 'I bought this book in 1910 because another copy of it had been a great favourite of us 4 children towards 1829–40. Gabriel was much enamoured of the designs by Martin & he continued throughout his life to regard this artist as a man of remarkable powers of invention.' [57]

In trying to see which world fathered Martin's imagination, it is impossible to pass by that strange world of the later eighteenth century, that of the Gothic Romance, and it is also clear that two of the most outstanding novels

of the type appeared outside their period. These are
Charles Robert Maturin's *Melmoth the Wanderer*, 1820,
and Mary Shelley's *Frankenstein*, 1818. It is perhaps with
the belated Gothic of *Frankenstein*, aware of the rumbling
engines outside the window and the galvanic experiments
in the next room, that we should associate Martin's
painting rather than with the purer Gothic of Strawberry
Hill and of the followers of Salvator Rosa with their
bandits in landscapes. Like the earlier novelists, however,
Martin made terrific emotive play with his landscapes and
natural phenomena; his figures are indolent in a vast
tranquillity, as *Adam and Eve entertaining the Archangel
Raphael* (Art Gallery, Kirkcaldy), or terrified actors in a
juggernaut melodrama, as in *The Fall of Babylon*, where
turgid murky clouds swirl up amongst the towers and
roof-gardens of the stricken city, but his *Satan presiding at
the Infernal Council* is indubitably lit by incandescent gas.

That Martin's use of extraordinary natural phenomena
was deliberate and that he stored memories of such
occurrences up against the day when he would require
them, is shown by a letter to Bulwer dealing with his
painting *Arthur and Ægte in the Happy Valley*, founded on
a passage in *King Arthur* by Bulwer, 'In endeavouring to
illustrate the poetry, I have represented a lovely night I
saw some twenty years ago, which was so remarkable for
the splendour of the heavenly bodies that, if I fail in doing
justice to the poet, I trust I shall please the astronomers,
as I have taken every pains to make my picture astro-
nomically correct'.[58]

For John Martin the Deluge was not so much a human
tragedy as an elemental upheaval in which the human
race, along with a myriad of animals, had had the misfortune to become involved, the victims of a scriptural
and astronomical cataclysm: his interest in man was not
in him as a sensate being, but as the ant-like creator of
colossal buildings and grandiose schemes—the Pyramids

I

were greater than any Pharaoh who ever ruled in Egypt; when he closed his eyes Martin could visualize the Tower of Babel but not Nimrod. His people perish in the ruins of a world too great for them to understand, and the vast pointless towers which they created become their tombstones.

REFERENCES

Sources of information about John Martin are: *The Reminiscences of John Martin, K.L.*, Leopold Charles Martin, in sixteen instalments in the *Newcastle Weekly Chronicle*, during the first quarter of 1889; *John Martin, Painter: His Life and Times*, Mary L. Pendered, London, 1923; and *John Martin, 1789–1854, Illustrator and Pamphleteer*, Thomas Balston, *Library*, Oxford, xiv, 4, March 1934, pp. 381–432. [A few copies also issued separately.] This last gives very important hand-lists of books containing engravings by, or after, John Martin, and of the various pamphlets by him and his brothers. In revising this article I have received inestimable help from a full-length typescript bibliography of John Martin, very kindly given to me by Mr. Balston. Mr. Balston is at present engaged in the preparation of a new life of the artist, with an appendix on his paintings by the present writer.

[1] *New Verse, An Anthology*, London, 1939, pp. 23–4.

[2] *The Life of John Ruskin*, E. T. Cook, London, 1911, i, 141–2.

[3] *Handbook to the Fine Art Collections in the International Exhibition*, F. T. Palgrave, London, 1862, p. 32.

[4] *Fraser's Magazine*, London, June 1843.

[5] *East Lynne*, Mrs. Henry Wood, Four Hundred and Eightieth Thousand, London, 1898, p. 367. [1861.]

[6] *Life of Benjamin Robert Haydon, from his autobiography and journals*, ed. Tom Taylor, London, 1853, ii, 188.

[7] *A New System of Natural Philosophy*, William Martin, Newcastle, 1821.

[8] *New Physico-Mechanical Experiments on the Spring and Weight of the Air*, Oxford, 1660.

[9] *Autobiographical Notes of the Life of William Bell Scott*, ed. W. Minto, London, 1892, i, 197.

[10] *The Last Days of the Antediluvian World, A Forlorn Hope, and Ishmael's Address*, London, 1830.

[11] Balston, *op. cit.*, p. 393.

[12] Letter to *The Times*, 15 December 1927.

[13] *Tilt's Monthly Magazine*, March 1833.

[14] Mr. Balston very kindly gave me a copy of this rare pamphlet. See also Thomas Balston, *The Life of Jonathan Martin*, London, 1945.

[15] Pendered, *op. cit.*, p. 220.

[16] *Reprint of Report of the Committee Appointed to take into consideration Mr. Martin's Plan for Rescuing the River Thames from every Species of Pollution* 1836, London. [c. 1845.]

[17] *Phytologia; or the Philosophy of Agriculture and Gardening*, London, 1800, pp. 242–3.

[18] See Reginald Reynolds, *Cleanliness and Godliness*, London, 1943; this book makes no mention of Martin's pioneer work on sanitation.

[19] *Thames and Metropolis Improvement Plan*, London, 1849, p. 36.

[20] *Outlines of Several New Inventions for Maritime and Inland Purposes*, John Martin, London, 1829.

[21] Pendered, *op. cit.*, p. 239.

[22] *Plan for Ventilating Coalmines*, John Martin, London, 1849.

[23] Pendered, *op. cit.*, p. 231.

[24] *Ibid.*, pp. 133–4.

[25] *Ibid.*, p. 232.

[26] *The Journal of Gideon Mantell, Surgeon and Geologist*, ed. E. Cecil Curwen, Oxford, 1940, p. 125.

[27] MS. note in my possession.

[28] Pendered, *op. cit.*, pp. 231–2.

[29] *A Divine and Prophetic Warning To The British Nation, and To The Whole World (First Published July, 1832), to which is added A Prophetic Vision of the Heavenly Jerusalem, and the Downfall of Babylon*, Δ Christian Magia, London, [?c. 1845].

[30] *A Descriptive Catalogue of the Engraving of the Deluge by John Martin*, London, 1828, p. 3.

31 *The Deluge*, John Martin, London, 4 April 1840.

32 Pendered, *op. cit.*, p. 133.

33 I owe this to the generosity of Mr. Balston.

34 *The Works of Thomas Lovell Beddoes*, ed. H. W. Donner, Oxford, 1935, p. 615; letter *c.* 7 March 1826.

35 *Romantic Painting in America*, James Thrall Soby and Dorothy C. Miller, New York, 1943, p. 13.

36 Pendered, *op. cit.*, p. 103.

37 *Essay on the Imaginative Faculty.*

38 *The Metaphysical Foundations of Physics*, E. A. Burtt, London and New York, 1925, p. 236.

39 *Washington Allston*, M. F. Sweetser, Boston, 1879, p. 121.

40 R. H. Dana, jun., quoted in *The Life and Letters of Washington Allston*, Jared B. Flagg, New York, 1892, p. 333. The wreckage of this obsessional work is now in the Museum of Fine Arts, Boston, Mass.

41 MS. note in my possession.

42 *Art in England*, 1800–1820, William T. Whitley, Cambridge, 1928, p. 258.

43 *Ibid.*, p. 320.

44 *England and the English*, E. Lytton Bulwer, London, 1833, ii, 205.

45 Pendered, *op. cit.*, p. 180.

46 *The Farington Diary*, ed. James Greig, London, 1922, etc., viii, 115.

47 *The Poetry and Prose of William Blake*, ed. Geoffrey Keynes, London, 1939 ed., p. 625.

48 *The Times*, 12 May 1828; my italics.

49 *Mirror*, 17 May 1828.

50 *My Autobiography and Reminiscences*, W. P. Frith, London, 1888, i, 47.

[51] Haydon, *ed. cit.*, ii, 100.

[52] *Life and Letters of William Bewick*, ed. Thomas Landseer, London, 1871, i, 71.

[53] Haydon, *ed. cit.*, ii, 89-90.

[54] *A Description of the Picture 'Belshazzar's Feast', painted by Mr. Martin, lately exhibited at the British Institution*, London, 1821.

[55] *Bulwer: A Panorama, Edward and Rosina, 1803–1836*, Michael Sadleir, London, 1931, pp. 332–5.

[56] Bulwer, *op. cit.*, ii, 211–12.

[57] Parker & Son, Oxford, *cat.* 54, 1934, and again in October 1943.

[58] Sadleir, *op. cit.*, p. 334.

INDEX

Date Due